D1111188

Marijuana: The World's Most Misunderstood Plant

A plant that has benefited mankind for at least 10,000 years and has even more promise for the future.

By: Jeffrey Friedland

Published By
Broome Publishing
350 West 50th Street, New York, NY 10019

Copyright © 2015 Jeffrey Friedland
All Rights Reserved

Library of Congress Cataloging in-Publication Data

Friedland, Jeffrey.
Marijuana: The World's Most Misunderstood Plant/Jeffrey Friedland
p.   cm.

Includes bibliographical references and index.

ISBN: 978-0-9893764-1-9 (pbk.)

1. Marijuana – History
2. Cannabis – History
3. Hemp – History
4. Marijuana – About the Plant
5. Cannabis: About the Plant
6. Hemp: About the Plant
7. Marijuana: Using the Plant
8. Cannabis: Using the Plant
9. Marijuana: Use as Medicine
10. Cannabis: Use as Medicine

First Edition

Set in Garamond

Cover Design by Miles Begin

While the author has made every effort to provide accurate Internet addresses for references and footnotes at the time of publication, neither the publisher nor the author assumes any responsibility for errors or changes that occur after publication. Further, the publisher does not have any control over and does not assume any responsibility for the author's or any third-party websites or their content.

To Richard Greenberg who embarked with me on this journey and provided the encouragement and motivation for me to understand the world's most misunderstood plant.

To my grandchildren, Julien, Wyatt, Violet and Zoe, it is my hope that you will have the opportunity to benefit from cannabis-based medicine.

"The illegality of cannabis is outrageous, an impediment to full utilization of a drug which helps produce the serenity and insight, sensitivity and fellowship so desperately needed in this increasingly mad and dangerous world."

Carl Sagan

Author's Notes:

Technically, the correct botanical name for this plant is cannabis. However, it is commonly referred to by a variety of slang or local names depending on the country or region.

In this book I have chosen to use the word cannabis when referring to the plant in a historical or scientific context and I use the word hemp to describe a plant that is cultivated for its fiber or the cannabinoid, cannabidiol, CBD.

The word marijuana only entered America's popular vocabulary in the early 1900s and then began to refer to the cannabis plant that provided psychoactive effects. Today, in North America, France and parts of Latin America, the plant is commonly referred to as marijuana, but in much of the rest of the world it is known as cannabis or hemp.

Reflecting the current common usage in the United States, I have generally used marijuana in this book to refer to the plant since the early 1920s.

The footnotes in the book are identified by Roman numerals. They provide definitions, details and clarifications and can be found at the bottom of the respective page.

I've included endnotes, identified with Arabic numbers, for the citations for quotes and sources. They can be accessed at the end of the book.

Contents

Author's Notes: i

Preface vi

Introduction: It's all about a Plant 3

PART ONE: The Misunderstood Marijuana Plant........................ 7

Chapter 1: What is Cannabis?.................................... 9

Chapter 2: A Source of Confusion: Cannabis, Marijuana, and Hemp... 13

Chapter 3: Why Marijuana Affects Us.................................... 16

Chapter 4: Trichomes, Terpenes, and Other Compounds 18

Chapter 5: Marijuana Varieties and Strains 23

PART TWO – Cannabis through the Ages................................. 29

Chapter 6: Why the History of Cannabis Matters................. 31

Chapter 7: Cannabis in Ancient Cultures and Civilizations ... 33

Chapter 8: Cannabis in Europe.................................... 43

Chapter 9: The Arrival of Cannabis in Latin America 45

Chapter 10: Cannabis Comes to North America 49

Chapter 11: The 1900s, The Movement to Ban Marijuana in the U.S... 53

Chapter 12: Marijuana in the Second Half of the 20th Century 67

Chapter 13: Marijuana in our Century 82

PART THREE: Breeding and Growing Marijuana 90

Chapter 14: Breeding Marijuana for Desired Characteristics 92

Chapter 15: Cultivating Marijuana 98

Chapter 16: Growing to Maximize the Plant's Quality 102

Chapter 17: The Marijuana Plant's Growth Cycle 106

PART FOUR – Consuming Marijuana 112

Chapter 18: Marijuana as a Psychoactive Substance 114

Chapter 19: Smoking Marijuana.......................................116

Chapter 20: Marijuana Concentrates and Extracts 118

Chapter 21: Marijuana Edibles 129

Chapter 22: Vaping and Dabbing......................................135

Chapter 23: Capsules, Topicals, and Tinctures...................139

PART FIVE: Marijuana-based Medicine 143

Chapter 24: Marijuana, Exiting the Shadows and Once Again Becoming Medicine after 80 Years......................................145

Chapter 25: Israel's History and Role in Marijuana Research 149

Chapter 26: The Key to Marijuana-Based Medicine: The Human Endocannabinoid System 155

Chapter 27: Cannabidiol or CBD, a Medical Game Changer159

Chapter 28: Medical Benefits from the Other Cannabinoids 165

Chapter 29: The Entourage or Whole Plant Effect 169

Chapter 30: Benefits of Marijuana-Based Medicine for Chronic Pain and Inflammation..173

Chapter 31: Marijuana-based Medicine for Specific Medical Conditions and Diseases..179

Acne and Skin Disorders 180

Attention Deficit Disorder and Attention Deficit Hyperactivity 181

Alzheimer's Disease 182

Amyotrophic lateral sclerosis (ALS) or Lou Gehrig's Disease 183

Anorexia 184

Anxiety 185

Arthritis 186

Asthma and Breathing Disorders 188

Autism 189

Bipolar Disorder 189

Cancer and the Side Effects of its Treatment Including Nausea 190

Crohn's Disease and Gastrointestinal Disorders 194

Depression 196

Endometriosis 197

Epilepsy and Seizures 198

Fibromyalgia 199

Glaucoma 200

HIV and AIDS 202

Lupus 203

Lyme Disease 204

Multiple Sclerosis 205

Narcotic Addiction 207

Parkinson's Disease 207

Post-Traumatic Stress Disorder (PTSD) 208

Schizophrenia 211

Sleep Disorders 212

Glossary 214

About Jeffrey Friedland 223

Acknowledgments 224

Index 226

Notes...228

Preface

The phrase Rocky Mountain High took on a whole new meaning on November 6, 2012. On that day, Amendment 64, a Colorado Ballot Initiative to legislate the "Use and Regulation of Marijuana" was approved by 56 percent of the state's voters. Despite strong vocal opposition from John Hickenlooper, the state's governor and many legislators, Colorado's constitution was formally amended to allow recreational marijuana, and was set to take effect on January 1, 2014.

The new law resulted in Colorado becoming the first state and the first government in the world to legalize recreational marijuana for adults. It wasn't just a local story. Colorado's new industry attracted national and international media coverage, and set the stage for other states that would follow in its footsteps.

Medical marijuana had been legal in Colorado since 2000. Colorado's medical marijuana regulations required patients to apply for a state-issued "red card" and to be registered in the state's medical marijuana registry. Patients were required to complete an application which included a physician certification that the patient had "a debilitating medical condition, which could be addressed by the use of marijuana." Over the years, many Colorado residents applied for and obtained red cards, others found the process too cumbersome to bother.

Colorado's recreational marijuana program had an entirely different set of rules than the state's medical marijuana program. It allowed anyone over the age of twenty-one, whether a Colorado resident or a visitor to the state, to legally purchase marijuana products from state-licensed recreational marijuana stores.

During the summer of 2013, I spoke with a friend, Richard Greenberg, about the prospects of Colorado's impending recreational marijuana industry. Richard was an environmental attorney and had been a co-founder of an environmental consulting firm, and like me, he was looking for a new challenge. Neither of us knew what to expect, but we decided to investigate Colorado's new industry further.

We traveled around the state meeting with owners of medical marijuana cultivation facilities and dispensaries. Almost everyone we spoke with hoped to change their medical marijuana licenses to recreational licenses as soon as they met the state's regulatory requirements. We also met with recreational marijuana "enthusiasts," who were excited about the opportunity to establish a legitimate business in a legal industry, after years of growing illegally.

The more meetings we had, the more apparent it became that there were going to be numerous opportunities in Colorado's new industry, despite the significant restrictions under the state's regulations. At the time, most of Colorado's medical grow facilities and dispensaries were not profitable; they lacked working capital and were struggling to survive. Many believed that a recreational market represented a significant opportunity for Colorado, not only for the growing and sale of marijuana but also for ancillary products, services and related technologies.

In December of 2013, we met two young entrepreneurs who lived in Breckenridge, one of Colorado's leading mountain resorts and ski towns. Brian Rogers and Caitlin McGuire owned an existing medical marijuana dispensary located on the town's Main Street, and a small indoor cultivation facility on the outskirts of town.

It was significant that Brian and Caitlin were already in the medical marijuana business, as initially the only participants who could obtain recreational cultivation and retail licenses when Colorado's recreational law was to take effect on January 1, 2014, were those who already had an existing licensed medical marijuana business.

Like so many small operators, Brian and Caitlin's business, the Breckenridge Cannabis Club, lacked the working capital to proceed with the conversion of their licenses from medical to recreational. They had been struggling financially due to the limitations and costs associated with complying with Colorado's medical marijuana regulations.

Right after Christmas in 2013, Richard and I made a loan to the Breckenridge Cannabis Club, with the intention that the loan would convert to ownership in the business once Richard and I were approved as owners by Colorado's Marijuana Enforcement Division.

At the time, Colorado's Marijuana Enforcement Division allowed a one-time conversion of medical marijuana inventory to recreational marijuana, in conjunction with an approved conversion of a medical marijuana license to a recreational license. Since it had been illegal to grow marijuana for recreational use until that time, without that provision, there would have been no inventory of recreational marijuana in Colorado on the first of January.

Brian and Caitlin used the funds we provided primarily to make a large wholesale purchase of marijuana so that they would have sufficient inventory when their license converted from medical to recreational.

The grand opening of the Breckenridge Cannabis Club on January 1, 2014, was a local, national and international media event. Hundreds of customers, including Colorado residents, skiers and tourists from the U.S. and around the world, came to Breckenridge and waited in line to buy marijuana when the law went into effect. Despite a snowstorm that New Year's Eve, the line to enter the store went down the steps and snaked into the street. Some people waited hours just to say they bought and used marijuana recreationally on the first day it was legal anywhere in the United States.

In the meantime, Richard and I had applied to become "approved" as owners by the state, an arduous process that ultimately took four months. First and foremost, we had to be Colorado residents for at least two years, which we were. Richard and I were then fingerprinted multiple times, and required to provide extensive financial information as well as answer in-depth background questionnaires. We were interviewed by an agent of the Colorado Marijuana Enforcement Division, who spoke to us while wearing a gun and handcuffs on his belt, a disquieting experience in itself. We also underwent background checks by both the Colorado Bureau of Investigation and the Federal Bureau of Investigation.

When many of our friends discovered that we were investing in Colorado's new industry, they also wanted to participate. However, once they learned the process required to become approved as owners by the state, it uniformly brought to a halt their desire to follow our lead.

Fifteen months later, in April 2015, the growing pains and travails of the Breckenridge Cannabis Club were highlighted in the eight-part television series, *High Profits* on CNN. In the network's promotional materials, CNN's description of the series stated, "Viewers will meet Brian Rogers and Caitlin McGuire: two business-minded, dream seeking, relentless visionaries with a plan unlike any other... The eight-part series...will grant exclusive access to the couple poised to be the first ever moguls of marijuana."

In February 2014, Richard, I and Tyler Burpee, a Toronto-based merchant banker, formed Global Cannabis Ventures as a Canadian corporation. We invested in three companies that intended to be approved as "licensed producers" under Canada's *Marihuana for Medical Purposes Regulations*, which were to become operational in April 2014. As of the writing of this book, during the fall of 2015, one of these companies has been approved as a licensed producer in Canada, and two are still awaiting approval.

The mission of Global Cannabis Ventures changed after a May 2014 lunch meeting Richard and I had with Dr. Alan Shackelford.

Our luncheon with Dr. Shackelford lasted almost three hours and resulted in a new course for our company. Dr. Shackelford shared with us a significant decision he had made -- to immigrate to Israel, where marijuana was an approved treatment option under the country's national healthcare system. He explained that his decision was influenced by the fact that marijuana remained classified as a Schedule I drug under the U.S. Controlled Substances Act, which made it virtually impossible to do any meaningful clinical research on marijuana in the U.S.

Dr. Shackelford shot to international fame in 2013 after being featured in CNN's *Weed* documentary as one of the two physicians who approved the use of medical marijuana for six-year-old Charlotte Figi. Charlotte suffered from Dravet syndrome, an incurable genetic disorder that results in continuous seizure activity which often leads to brain damage. Charlotte's symptoms were largely alleviated thanks to treatment with the extracts of a strain of marijuana with a very low content of the psychoactive cannabinoid, THC, and a high content of the non-psychoactive cannabinoid, CBD. Charlotte's success with the CBD treatment was soon duplicated with other Dravet patients, and the low-CBD strain of marijuana became known as "Charlotte's Web."

Our lunch conversation with Dr. Shackelford convinced both of us to change the course of Global Cannabis Ventures. We came away from that meeting with a decision to primarily focus on medical marijuana rather than the recreational use of the plant. We recognized that recreational marijuana would likely grow to be a large industry, but concluded that there would be greater long-term potential for the medical marijuana industry.

Richard and I were already well aware of the contributions Israel had made to marijuana research, so once we decided to refocus Global Cannabis Ventures on the medical side of marijuana, we knew that it meant a trip to Israel.

That June we flew to Israel and met with scientists, researchers and physicians, and eventually invested in two companies. The first was planning clinical trials for several proprietary marijuana-based medicines, and the second had developed a platform to facilitate the genetic analysis and breeding of marijuana plants. To paraphrase Dr. Shackelford, our desire was to become involved in "real medicine, based on real science."

In September of 2014, we changed the company's name to INTIVA Inc. and continued our focus on the medical cannabis industry. As of the writing of this book during the fall of 2015, INTIVA has established a financial services business that leases extraction equipment to marijuana growers in California, developed a line of CBD-based topicals, and acquired an agricultural property to lease to marijuana growers in Colorado.

Throughout our journey, we have continuously been asked about marijuana, why we decided to get involved in the industry, if we really believe marijuana has medicinal value, and what we hope to accomplish.

Marijuana: The World's Most Misunderstood Plant, is the result of the dozens of meeting and conversations I've had, speeches I've given, and my view of the marijuana industry as an emerging market.

I hope this book will provide an introduction and overview of the exciting marijuana industry and the tremendous potential of a misunderstood plant that has benefited mankind for 10,000 years.

Jeffrey Friedland

JEFFREY FRIEDLAND

JEFFREY FRIEDLAND

Introduction: It's all about a Plant

Ganja, weed, grass, hemp, marijuana, Mary Jane; call it what you will, there has never been a plant as misunderstood as marijuana. Nor has there been a plant with as much potential for mankind.

Originating in Central Asia and the foothills of the Himalayas, cannabis was one of man's earliest cultivated crops. It has been grown for a multitude of uses over thousands of years. Cannabis is a source for fiber, oil, and herbal medicines. It has been used for religious and spiritual purposes, and yes, it is also a psychoactive substance.

Cannabis fibers have been found in pottery shards estimated to date back more than 10,000 years. The earliest records documenting the use of marijuana are from the Chinese Emperor Shen Nung, who lived around 2800 B.C. Shen Nung was considered the patron deity of agriculture and is credited with the discovery of cannabis as a therapeutic agent.

Cannabis first came to the Western hemisphere during the colonization of the Americas where its fiber was important for the production of rope, clothing and paper. Cannabis was an essential

3

herbal medicine in Europe and the United States in the 1800s and was even added to the official U.S. Pharmacopeia in 1850.[1]

Even though cannabis was valued for its medicinal properties, by the turn of the 20th century American attitudes toward cannabis, which was increaslingly being known as marijuana, started to change. The movement to ban alcohol that led to prohibition, also influenced attitudes toward cannabis. The use of marijuana for recreational purposes by immigrants and later by African-Americans and entertainers also contributed to the negative views and subjected the plant to increasing attacks.

As the 1900s wore on, a movement to ban marijuana was gaining momentum worldwide. Led by the United States, this effort was delegated to the newly created Federal Bureau of Narcotics. Under the direction of its zealous commissioner, Harry Anslinger, the Bureau promoted legislation that eventually banned marijuana in the U.S. in 1937. The removal of cannabis-based medicine from the U.S. Pharmacopeia in 1942, eliminated the plant as an approved source of medicine. By 1960, marijuana was illegal throughout most of the world.

Although governments were successful in outlawing marijuana, the debate regarding its value continued. And although it was illegal, marijuana remained popular with many users. It was viewed as a symbol of peace and rebellion, thanks to the hippie generation, and a gateway to addiction courtesy of the War on Drugs.

Despite the concerns surrounding marijuana use, mainstream sentiment continued to change -- more than half of adult Americans now favor legalizing it. Scientific and medical research are providing a greater understanding of the effects of marijuana on the human body, and the value of marijuana-based medicine.

Over the past two decades, the movement to legalize or decriminalize marijuana gained momentum. Led by patients and families who directly experienced the therapeutic and health

---

[1] A pharmacopeia is a book listing medicines and their uses, typically published by a government or a medical society.

benefits of the plant, the medicinal properties derived from marijuana are now being acknowledged by many healthcare providers and policy makers.

Proponents of the plant's recreational use are also being heard. The key argument for legalization and decriminalization is that marijuana is far less problematic for society than alcohol. In some states, citizens have voted to change laws. In other states, citizens have demanded action by their elected officials. This has led to the legalization of marijuana for both medical and recreational purposes in an increasing number of U.S. states, territories and Native American tribal lands.

JEFFREY FRIEDLAND

PART ONE: The Misunderstood Marijuana Plant

JEFFREY FRIEDLAND

Chapter 1: What is Cannabis?

Cannabis is part of the Cannabaceae family of flowering plants, which also includes hops and hackberries. Flowering plants are usually either male or female, both of which are needed to breed plants that produce seeds.[I] However, only unfertilized female plants produce flowers. Since flowers are the primary source of the cannabinoids, the plant's active chemical compounds, female plants are generally more popular with growers.

There are three subspecies of Cannabis plants: sativa, indica, and ruderalis.[II] The subspecies differ in height, stature, branch length, leaf size and structure, bud size and density, flowering time, odor, and psychoactive effects.[III]

The original classification of Cannabis was established in 1785 by the French biologist Jean-Baptiste Lamarck. He observed

---

[I] Although not a normal occurrence, cannabis plants can be hermaphrodite and have both male and female characteristics.
[II] Plant family and genus names are always capitalized. So, "Cannabis" is capitalized when referring to the genus.
[III] Based on the genetic markers on the three subspecies, in 2014, Dr. John McPartland suggested that the three subspecies have been incorrectly named and should be renamed based on where they originated. However, the cannabis industry has not adopted McPartland's renaming scheme.

that certain cannabis plants from India were intoxicating and could be made into hashish, whereas the cannabis plants common to Europe had no mind-altering or psychoactive effect.

The variation in these characteristics is thought to have evolved as a result of the plant's genetic makeup and the environmental conditions where it developed. The cross-breeding of these three subspecies has led to the large number of hybrid cannabis strains that exist today.

Cannabis indica

It's generally thought that Cannabis indica originated in the mountainous Hindu Kush region that stretches between central Afghanistan and northern Pakistan.

Indica plants are typically stocky and densely-branched with short and wide leaves. The buds of indica plants tend to be wide, dense and bulky. This Cannabis subspecies developed thick coats of resin as protection against the harsh mountain climate, resulting in a higher ratio of the psychoactive cannabinoid THC, to that of CBD, compared to strains derived from sativa plants.

Cannabis sativa

Cannabis sativa originated in tropical regions that were close to the equator. These plants are loosely branched, with long, narrow, leaves and long, finger-shaped flowers.

Sativa plants were originally bred for height to maximize the length of their fibrous stalks and often reach a height of twenty feet.

Cannabis ruderalis

Cannabis ruderalis is the least common Cannabis subvariety. It is a wild subspecies, first named in 1942 by the Russian botanist, D. E. Janischevisky.

Similar to sativa plants, ruderalis has minimal amounts of THC, and its short stature makes it less attractive for its fiber. Since it originated in central Russia, ruderalis is extremely hardy, and its autoflowering characteristics make it attractive for cross-breeding with other strains.[1]

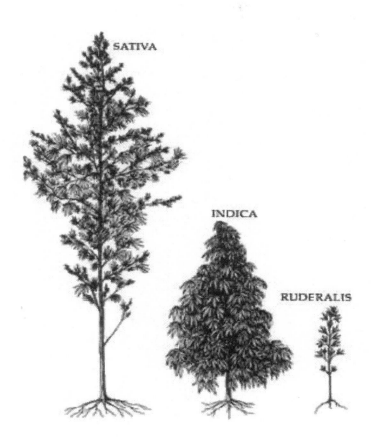

SATIVA

INDICA

RUDERALIS

---

[1] The auto-flowering Cannabis ruderalis subspecies starts to flower when it reaches a certain maturity, regardless of its exposure to light and darkness.

JEFFREY FRIEDLAND

Chapter 2: A Source of Confusion: Cannabis, Marijuana, and Hemp

The major reason that cannabis is the world's most misunderstood plant is because of its various names and the confusion between them. The words are often used interchangeably, adding to the confusion, however, cannabis, hemp, and marijuana are all members of the same plant species or genus, Cannabis.

The plant is also Cannabis regardless of its content of psychoactive cannabinoids. Non-psychoactive varieties of cannabis commonly referred to as hemp, were outlawed in much of the world at the same time that the psychoactive form of the plant was banned.

There are two basic categories of marijuana plants, those that evolved in northern climates and those grown predominantly closer to the equator. The hardier, northern plants are generally referred to as hemp, and are grown primarily for the production of fibers and oils, and the medical benefits of their non-psychoactive cannabinoid, CBD. Plants originating in warmer climates are typically grown for their psychoactive and medicinal properties. Still referred to as cannabis in much of the world, they are also referred to as marijuana, particulalry in the Americas.

What is Marijuana?

The derivation of the word marijuana is generally thought to have originated from Mexican slang and was originally spelled variously as mariguana or marihuana. Its definition is "Maria" (Mary), "Juana" (Joan or Jane), which has led to today's English slang, "Mary Jane."[I]

The association of the word marijuana with the psychoactive varieties of the cannabis plant first spread from Mexico to other Spanish-speaking countries. The word then made its way into the common vocabulary of other languages including French and English.

The name, marijuana, was popularized in the 1930s when the U.S. government and news media began a relentless attack on the use of cannabis.

In many parts of the world, including the Americas, "marijuana" was used to describe strains of cannabis grown for their psychoactive properties.

What Is Hemp?

This cannabis plant variety typically has long fibrous stalks, rather than the large, resinous cannabinoid producing buds found in the more psychoactive strains of the cannabis plant.[II]

Similar to bamboo, hemp is a renewable plant with numerous commercial uses. It is a good source of oil and fiber for cloth, paper, and rope. Its seeds are full of Omega 3 and 6, are high in nutritional fiber, and contain the mineral magnesium. Hemp can be used as an additive to strengthen concrete, as an insulation material and as a source of bio-based plastics. It is also a renewable source of energy.

[I] This spelling, marihuana was more common in the early 1900s. Countries including Canada and the United States have also used the spelling "marihuana" as an official spelling in laws and regulations.
[II] Industrial hemp also contains THC, but the quantity is minimal, typically less than 0.3%.

Today's generally accepted international definition of hemp was developed by the Canadian scientist, Ernest Small in 1971. Small published *The Species Problem in Cannabis* in 1978.[1] In it, Small stated that it was impossible to determine scientifically a natural point along the spectrum of cannabinoid content that could distinguish strains of marijuana from strains of hemp. Despite this conclusion, he proceeded to make an arbitrary distinction between the two plants.

Small decided that cannabis plants with a THC level of more than 0.3 percent were marijuana. Those plants with less than that amount he determined were "industrial hemp."[1] This 0.3 percent limit of THC became a de facto and often legal standard globally for industrial hemp.

At the time of its publication, Small's book garnered minimal attention. However, his differentiation between hemp and marijuana inadvertently influenced the legal future of hemp in the United States and many other countries.

It is Small's arbitrary dividing point that continues to cause confusion and contributes to the misunderstanding of the qualities of hemp.

---

[1] In many parts of the world "hemp" can refer both to the fiber producing varieties of cannabis as well as varieties of the plant grown for their psychoactive properties. The term "industrial hemp" came into common and often legal use to denote a cannabis plant without psychoactive properties.

Chapter 3: Why Marijuana Affects Us

There are an estimated 594 chemical compounds in the marijuana plant. The most important of these are phytochemicals, referred to as cannabinoids.[1] Researchers have identified 111 of these cannabinoids to-date, and it is likely that more are yet to be discovered.[2]

The two main cannabinoids that affect humans are THC and CBD. The psychoactive THC provides the high for recreational users and spiritual experiences. THC also has many medicinal and health benefits, most importantly its ability to relieve pain.

CBD is not a psychoactive cannabinoid, but recent research indicates that it also provides numerous medical and health benefits. These include its use as an anti-inflammatory agent and its ability to treat seizure activity.

The question is, why do THC and CBD have such a profound effect on us?

Roger Adams, head of the Department of Chemistry at the University of Illinois, in Champagne-Urbana, was one of America's leading organic chemists. In 1940, he received a red oil extract derived from wild hemp grown in Minnesota from the U.S.

---

[1] Phytochemicals are chemical compounds that occur naturally in plants.

government for research. From that plant extract, Adams discovered and identified the cannabinoid, cannabidiol or CBD.

In 1964, Dr. Raphael Mechoulam, an Israeli postdoctoral student, had an interest in the biological activity of natural substances. Mechoulam and his colleagues were determined to isolate the psychoactive component of marijuana, and their research led to the discovery of the chemical compound D9-tetrahydrocannabinol, which was given the shorthand designation, THC.

With the mystery of what caused the psychoactivity solved, another was raised. How and why did THC affect the human body? It took almost another 25 years for researchers to answer that question.

In 1988, a research team, led by Dr. Allyn Howlett, at St. Louis University School of Medicine, discovered that THC was binding with receptors that were prevalent throughout the human body. These receptors were named "cannabinoid receptors."

Howlett's discovery was the impetus for scientists to search for the biological purpose of the receptors. Subsequent research identified two endogenous cannabinoids; Anandamide and 2-AG. Research indicated that these endogenous cannabinoids, or endocannabinoids, influenced pain, appetite, motor learning and the strength or weakness of signals between cells. Because these cannabinoids were produced internally in the human body, or endogenously, the network of receptors and binding agents was named the endocannabinoid system.

Additional research concluded that cannabinoids produced outside the human body, or "exogenously", such as the CBD and THC from marijuana, mimicked endocannabinoids. These cannabinoids bind with the receptors in the endocannabinoid system to mitigate pain, suppress nausea, decrease pressure and enhance appetite. Scientists have since sought to unravel the details of the endocannabinoid system and its implications for marijuana-based medicine.

Chapter 4: Trichomes, Terpenes, and Other Compounds

Trichomes

Like many other plants, marijuana plants are covered with tiny, hair-like cilia, which are called trichomes.[1] Although they look like fine hairs, they are actually small glands which blanket the plant. Trichomes give marijuana the frosty appearance, often making the surface of the plant appear white or silver.

I Cilia are small hair-like structures that extend from certain plant cells, including on the edges of some leaves forming a fringe.

There are a few different types of trichomes. The most prevalent are glandular trichomes which produce and store the terpenes and cannabinoids. There is a general misconception that the marijuana plant produces cannabinoids that are contained in the plant itself. This is not the case. All cannabinoids are found on the surface of the plant, in the trichomes.

Trichomes have several biological purposes in the development and survival of Cannabis plants.

They secrete aromatic oils and compounds that attract bees and other pollinating insects. They provide insulation for the plant, protecting it from high winds and low humidity, and act as a natural sunscreen, shielding the plant from harmful UV-B light rays.[1]

Trichomes create a physical barrier, making it difficult for beetles and other pests to reach the plant's seeds. In addition, the psychoactive properties of THC induce a high when ingested by insects which distracts them from eating the plant. A similar protective system can be found in opium-producing poppies and in some mushrooms.

---

[1] Sunlight is made up of two types of harmful rays, long wave ultraviolet A (UVA) and short wave ultraviolet B (UVB).

Decades of breeding marijuana for its psychoactive properties has resulted in strains that consistently produce more of these gooey, resinous, trichomes. Regardless of whether the marijuana plant is high or low in THC or CBD, its trichomes contain these two cannabinoids and the other 109 cannabinoids.

Tetrahydrocannabinol or THC

The most well-known cannabinoid in marijuana plants is tetrahydrocannabinol, or Delta-9-tetrahydrocannabinol, commonly referred to as THC. It is the cannabinoid responsible for the psychoactive effect of marijuana, and until recently, the only cannabinoid that most breeders, growers, and users were interested in.

In addition to its psychoactivity, THC also provides numerous medical benefits. Scientific research is still in the early stages, but there are many indications that THC has mild to moderate analgesic effects, can be useful for pain treatment, is beneficial as an antioxidant, and can stimulate appetite.

THC also induces a relaxed state and often impacts a person's sense of smell, hearing and eyesight. Research studies indicate that THC can be effective for the treatment of nausea and as an anti-emetic, to forestall vomiting, which is why it often used to help cancer patients manage the effects of chemotherapy. THC can also cause fatigue, and for some people, may reduce aggression.

Cannabidiol or CBD

The second best-known cannabinoid is cannabidiol, or CBD. Recent studies indicate that CBD has tremendous potential as a treatment for numerous diseases and medical conditions. Research is at an early-stage, but the medical benefits of CBD are provided, either by itself, with THC, or with some of the plant's other cannabinoids in what has been referred to as the "whole plant" or "entourage effect."[1]

Before 2013, most attention regarding the medical benefits of the marijuana plant was focused on THC. Since 2013 CBD has generated media attention, and the interest of healthcare providers and patients because of indications of its medical benefits. These include the reduction of epileptic seizure activity in children.

CBD research is also at an early stage, however, studies indicate that the cannabinoid can relieve the symptoms of nausea, and is beneficial for anxiety, inflammation and convulsions. Some preliminary studies indicate that CBD may also inhibit the growth of cancer cells.

Other Cannabinoids in the Marijuana Plant

While THC and CBD are the best-known and most prevalent, researchers have already identified an additional 109 cannabinoids in the Cannabis species, although the quantity of these "lesser" cannabinoids is often minimal.

Minor cannabinoids include cannabidiolic acid (CBDA), cannabinol (CBN), cannabigerol (CBG), cannabichromene (CBC),

---

[1] The "entourage effect" was a term invented in 2011 by Dr. Ethan Russo, who described it in the British Journal of Pharmacology as the synergistic contributions of other compounds in marijuana.

cannabidivarin (CBDV), tetrahydrocannabivarin (THCV), and tetrahydrocananbinolic Acid (THCA).

Terpenes

Terpenes are organic hydrocarbons that provide marijuana plants with their scent and color. Not unlike other strong-smelling plants and flowers, terpenes in marijuana evolved for survival purposes, specifically to repel predators and lure pollinators. Pungent terpenoid oils repel insects and animal grazers and others prevent fungus.

Recent research on marijuana's biochemistry indicates that terpenes are involved in the production of cannabinoids, serving as starting compounds in the biosynthetic pathway. This biochemical process occurs in the plant's trichomes.

There are many factors that influence a marijuana plant's development of terpenes. These include climate, weather, age and maturation, fertilizer application, and soil type.

To date, an estimated 200 terpenes have been discovered in marijuana, resulting in the variance in a plant's fragrance from strain-to-strain. Marijuana researchers have begun to focus on the pharmacological importance of terpenes, which form the basis of marijuana-based aromatherapy.

Chapter 5: Marijuana Varieties and Strains

The difference between a Cannabis subspecies and a variety is one of semantics. Even botanists and taxonomists often use the words interchangeably.

This book uses "subspecies" to refer to indica, sativa or ruderalis, which are subspecies of the genus Cannabis. It uses "strain" to indicate a plant bred as a hybrid of a subspecies. A "variety" indicates a plant's origination, specifically if it was grown from seed, a clone or in the wild.

Marijuana Varieties

There are four basic varieties of marijuana plants.

"Clone-Only Varieties" are genetically identical clones of the parent plant. This is the most popular commercial method of propagating marijuana plants.

"Stable Seed Varieties" are plants bred by creating a genetically stable variety from seeds. It involves selectively choosing male and female plants with specific qualities, which are then bred over multiple generations. The objecitve is to cultivate a stable generation whose seeds will consistently grow plants that exhibit the selected characteristics.

"Unstable seed varieties" are plants grown from seeds that were not bred for specific characteristics. Plants grown from unstable seed varieties typically present a wide variety of characteristics and no uniformity.

"Wild races or landraces," refer to varieties such as Thai or Colombian, plants that have been found growing in the wild in certain regions. These plants are often used in the breeding of specialized strains.

Marijuana Strains

A strain is a designated group of marijuana plants that are either descended from a modified plant which is produced by conventional breeding, by utilizing biotechnology, or which results from a genetic mutation.

Strains are bred to intensify certain desired characteristics of a plant. Frequently the most desired characteristics are the percentages of specific cannabinoids. Typically, plants are bred for levels of THC and/or CBD for medicinal purposes, or levels of THC for psychoactivity.

The creation of a unique strain can be very beneficial for the breeder. It can provide a valuable revenue stream if the strain becomes popular, as well as brand recognition for the breeder. The creation of new strains with distinctive characteristics is very competitive between marijuana breeders.

Once a pure strain has been developed it is usually named by the breeder. From a business perspective, the naming of a strain is an important component of the breeder's marketing strategy. Breeders frequently give their strains distinct and memorable names. This is done to differentiate new proprietary strain from strains already in the marketplace. The name may also provide knowledgeable consumers and marijuana connoisseurs with an indication of the plant's properties, including its color, taste, smell or genealogical parentage.

There are also local and regional variations in the names of strains. The same strain marketed under one name in Colorado may be sold under a different name in California or Amsterdam.

As of this writing, the Internet website, Leafly, highlights more than 300 sativa, more than 435 indica, and more than 700 hybrid strains, however, it's questionable how many of these strains are truly distinct.[3]

Sativa Strains

Sativa plants are tall and loosely branched and typically have long, narrow leaves. Buds of sativa strains tend to have a grassier odor than buds of indica strains.

Popular sativa strains include Acapulco Gold, Diesel, Sour Diesel, Green Crack, Haze, Super Silver Haze, Durban Poison, Jack Herer, Malawi Gold, Sour and Lemon Diesel.

Indica Strains

Pure indica strains are shorter and bushier and have wider leaflets than sativa strains. Indica strains are preferred by many indoor growers due to their manageable size. Indica strains often take a month or two shorter to mature than sativa strains.

Popular indica strains include BC Bud, Kush, Bubba Kush, Northern Lights, Skywalker, Romulan, Death Star, Blue Cheese, Granddaddy Purple, Blackberry Kush, Afghan Kush, and Purple Kush.

Hybrid Strains

In addition to pure indica, sativa and ruderalis strains, hybrid strains that are bred to exhibit traits from both of a plant's parents are increasingly popular.

A popular hybrid strain that was bred for medical purposes is Charlotte's Web, a Cannabis sativa strain with less than 0.3percent THC. It has gained popularity as an option for treating children suffering from seizures.

Another example of a hybrid strain is White Widow, which was first bred in the Netherlands from a Brazilian landrace ruderalis and a resin-heavy South Indian indica.

Lowryder is another popular hybrid strain. It retains the autoflowering behavior of ruderalis plants while also producing appreciable amounts of both THC and CBD.

Breeders also incorporate popular hybrids into new strains to capitalize on the demand for specific traits of the parents' strains. In many instances, the new hybrid will be named after the parent strain. This is particularly common with Haze, Diesel, and Sour strains, with new derivative strain such as Purple Haze, NYC Diesel, Sour Diesel, Super Sour Diesel, Sage N Sour and Miami Haze.

Kush Strains

Kush strains are worthy of special attention, because of both their legendary history and their contribution to some of today's most important and popular strains. Kush strains evolved due to centuries of natural and human selection. The resulting indica plants are naturally short and stocky with large and resinous trichomes.

Kush strains began their voyage around the world in the 1960s and early 1970s. Travelers on what became known as the "hippie trail" brought seeds of kush strains back to Canada, the United States, and Europe.

Some of the descendants of these Kush strains, Afghani, Kush, and Skunk, changed the marijuana industry forever.

Because indica-dominant plants have shorter flowering times, it was possible for growers to succeed in growing Kush strains in northern climates, even as far north as Alaska.

Not all cannabis strains with Kush in the name are genetic descendants of the legendary Hindu Kush region; some are hybrids or sativa-dominant strains.

While Kush has lost some of its historical meaning, Kush strains that are the "real thing" are valued by many discerning medical and recreational consumers.

Popular Kush strains include Purple Kush, OG Kush, Lemon Kush, Pineapple Kush and Cotton Candy Kush.

PART TWO – Cannabis through the Ages

JEFFREY FRIEDLAND

Chapter 6: Why the History of Cannabis Matters

The oldest confirmed use of cannabis dates back more than 10,000 years. And while it is most commonly known for its psychoactive properties as an herbal medicine, a component of religious and spiritual ceremonies, and as a recreational substance, cannabis is actually an incredibly versatile plant. It was a key crop in most regions of the world.

These uses may be less common today, however throughout history cannabis has been used to create textiles, rope, paper, paint, varnish, food, soap, furniture, fuel, animal feed, and plastics. The list goes on and on. American colonists even used it as currency.

With this rich history, it is difficult to believe that it was illegal to grow, process, sell or possess cannabis in most of the western world, including the United States, until very recently. Today, the plant is illegal in more places than where it is legal. When the history of cannabis is written in the future, the plant's illegality over the past almost eight decades will likely be viewed as a strange anomaly.

The abbreviated account that follows illustrates cannabis' tie to the development of civilization throughout the past 10,000 years in China, the Indian sub-continent, Europe and the Americas.[1]

---

[1] It is generally agreed that the earliest use of a written language was in Mesopotamia around 3200 B.C, followed by China around 1200 B.C. The history of the use of cannabis that precedes these dates is based on archeological evidence and later writings.

Chapter 7: Cannabis in Ancient Cultures and Civilizations

Remnants of cannabis have been discovered at sites where prehistoric hunters and gatherers lived. It flourished in their nutrient-rich waste sites, leading researchers to believe it is among humanity's oldest cultivated crops.[4]

Cannabis in Ancient China

There are divergent positions as to how the cannabis plant evolved, but the prevalent consensus is that it originated on the steppes of Central Asia and in the foothills of the Himalayas.[1]

The Chinese Emperor Fu Hsi, who it is believed lived approximately 2900 B.C., is credited with being one of the founders of China's Middle Kingdom. He is also attributed with bringing civilization to China. Legends state that Fu Hsi was the first to use the word Ma, the Chinese world for cannabis. He asserted that cannabis was a medicine and that it possessed both yin and yang, male and female properties.

---

[1] Another opinion is that cannabis evolved in what is now Siberia and Mongolia.

The Chinese Emperor Shen Nung, also referred to as Chen Nug, lived around 2700 B.C. and is considered to be the father of Chinese medicine. Nung is generally credited with discovering the healing properties of cannabis as well as ginseng and ephedra.[1]

A Chinese pictogram showed hemp growing in a shed.

The earliest written reference to the medical properties of cannabis was in the Rh-Ya, the Chinese pharmacopeia, which dates from approximately the 15th century B.C. The Rh-Ya is considered the world's oldest pharmacopeia. An extensive list of herbal remedies, it is considered to be a compilation of medicines that had been passed down orally for generations. The Rh-Ya recommends cannabis for more than 100 ailments, including gout, rheumatism, malaria, and absentmindedness.[5]

The earliest known physical evidence of cannabis dates to approximately 700 B.C. Cannabis was discovered in the burial tomb of a Caucasoid male dressed as a shaman.[6] This discovery was made in China's remote northwest, bordering Russia in what is now known as the Xinjiang Uyghur Autonomous Region. Researchers have concluded that the cannabis found in the tomb was clearly cultivated for psychoactive purposes rather than for use as fiber for clothing or food. The Chinese physician and surgeon Hua Tue, sometimes referred to as Hua T'o, lived approximately 145 to 208 A.D., and is often referred to as the "god of surgery."[II] His accomplishments were well documented. He is best known for his surgical operations and use of mafeisan as an herbal

---

[I] The plant ephedra sinica, known in Chinese as ma huang 麻黃.
[II] He is also referred to as Hua T'o.

anesthetic formulation.[1] It is generally acknowledged that cannabis was a primary ingredient in mafeisan.

Zhang Zhongjing, who lived from 150 to 219 AD, was a Han Dynasty physician. He established the principles for using medications and documented medical practices. He wrote two classic texts, the *Treatise of Febrile Diseases Caused by Cold and Miscellaneous Diseases* and *Synopsis of Prescriptions of the Golden Chamber.* Both referenced the use of pills made from cannabis as a cure for constipation, and "spleen restriction."

In the Chinese medical text, *Bencao Gangmu Materia Medica*, written in 1578 by Li Shizhen, the use of cannabis was described as a treatment for vomiting, parasitic infections and hemorrhages. Around the same time, cannabis was widely used in China for a variety of medical conditions, including diarrhea, dysentery, and as an appetite stimulant.[7]

Cannabis in the Ancient Middle East

When cannabis is thought of, frequently one of the first things that comes to mind is hashish. Hashish, or hash as it's commonly known, originated in the Middle East, where cannabis has been intertwined with the region's history.

Cannabis was used by the ancient Egyptians for a variety of disorders. It was used as an eye treatment, probably to treat glaucoma, as well as an anti-inflammatory, and it was also used to administer enemas. Egyptian use of cannabis was confirmed when cannabis pollen was found on the mummy of Rameses II, who died in approximately 1213 B.C.

In a burial tomb in Beit Shemesh, which is located between Jerusalem and Tel Aviv in modern-day Israel, the skeleton of an approximately 14-year-old girl was found along with bronze coins dating from the 4th century. Contained in her pelvic area was the

---

[1] Mafeisan (麻沸散), literally "cannabis boil powder," was the world's first documented general anesthetic.

skeleton of a term fetus. The fetus was of a size that would have precluded a successful vaginal delivery. In her abdominal area gray carbonized material was found and analyzed, which showed a presence of THC. The conclusion of archeologists and researchers was that cannabis was used as part of an unsuccessful attempt at delivery, likely paralleling a similar usage in ancient Egypt.

Cannabis also has a long history throughout the Arab world, seemingly following the spread of Islam. Rhazès, an historically significant Islamic physician, prescribed cannabis in the ninth century.[8] He recommended it as an analgesic and anesthetic, as well as suggesting its use for numerous medical conditions including syphilis and migraines.

Cannabis in Religious Texts

There is debate among biblical scholars regarding references to the possible use of cannabis in the Bible and other religious texts. Physical evidence confirms the medical use of cannabis in ancient Israel during the time of the Old and New Testaments. Examination of the etymology of the different words for cannabis supports that evidence.

The word cannabis is the same in Latin, which was derived from the Greek κάνναβις (kánnabis), which was originally a Scythian or Thracian word.[I] The Semitic etymologist Sula Benet, of the Institute of Anthropological Sciences in Warsaw, indicated the origin of the word cannabis to be the Hebrew word קניבוס (qannabbôs or kaneh bosm).[II] Benet stated:

> The astonishing resemblance between the Semitic 'kanbos' and the Scythian "cannabis" lead me to suppose that the Scythian word was of Semitic origin. These etymological discussions run parallel to arguments drawn from history.

The Iranian Scythians were probably related to the Medes, who were neighbors of the Semites and could easily have assimilated the word for hemp. The Semites, including the ancient

---

[I] The Scythians were a nomadic Indo-European people.
[II] She also went by the name of Sara Benetowa.

Hebrews, likely spread the word during their migrations through Asia Minor.[9]

Cannabis in the Old Testament

The Hebrew Bible's Old Testament contained references to the use of cannabis as a fiber, as a source of rope and cloth, and as incense. There is also evidence that cannabis was the active ingredient in the holy anointing oils of both the Old and New Testaments, where it was used to separate the sacred from the secular.

Exodus 30:22-23 describes Moses receiving instructions from God to anoint the meeting tent and all its furnishings with specially prepared oil.[10]

"Moreover the Lord spake unto Moses, saying,

*Take thou also unto thee principal spices, of pure myrrh five hundred shekels, and of sweet cinnamon half so much, even two hundred and fifty shekels, and of **Kaneh-Bosm** two hundred and fifty shekels,*

And of cassia five hundred shekels, after the shekel of sanctuary, and of oil olive a hin:

And thou shalt make it an oil of holy ointment, an ointment compound after the art of the apothecary: it shall be a holy anointing oil.

And thou shalt anoint the tabernacle of the congregation therewith, and the ark of the testimony,

And the table and all his vessels, and the candlestick and his vessels, and the altar of incense,

And the altar of burnt offering with all his vessels, and the laver and his foot.

And thou shalt sanctify them, that they may be most holy: whatsoever toucheth them shall be holy.

And thou shalt anoint Aaron and his sons, and consecrate them, that they may minister unto me in the priest's office.

And thou shalt speak unto the children of Israel, saying, this shall be a holy anointing oil unto me throughout your generations.

There are two other references to kaneh in the Hebrew Bible, commonly translated as sweet cane, in Isaiah 43:24 and Jeremiah 6:20.

Kaneh-bosem is also referenced in the Old Testament books of Jeremiah and Ezekiel. In both, the King James translation mistranslated kaneh-bosem as the plant calamus, just as it had in its translation of the plant in the Book of Exodus.

Cannabis in the New Testament

Archeologists have discovered vessels with cannabis residue, dating from the time of Jesus, in both what was ancient Judea and Egypt.

Anointing oil was used to help cure people suffering from crippling diseases. A cannabis-based anointing oil could have been absorbed into the body when rubbed on the skin. This may have been beneficial for people with a variety of medical problems.

It was written in the New Testament that Jesus:

... anointed [his disciples] with [a] potent entheogenic oil, sending out the twelve apostles to do the same.[1]

After Jesus' death, the disciple James suggested that anyone of the Christian community who was sick should be anointed by the elders with oil in the name of Jesus.

While not a mainstream view, there is also speculation that the use of a cannabis-based oil or chrism, could have resulted in Jesus' spiritual visions.[II] There is even some speculation that the

---

[I] Entheogenic oils are chemical substances, typically of plant origin, that are ingested to produce an altered state of consciousness for religious or spiritual purposes. From the Greek, literally 'becoming divine within.'

[II] Chrism is a Greek word literally meaning "an anointing," and is a holy anointing oil, or "consecrated oil", used by many Christian religions including the Roman Catholic Church, Eastern Orthodox Church, Anglican Communion, Oriental Orthodox Church and Armenian Apostolic Church.

miracles attributed to Jesus and his disciples may actually have been due to the healing effects of this cannabis extract.

Cannabis in the Indian Sub-Continent and Persia

Beginning about 1800 B.C. cannabis was brought to the Indian subcontinent with the Aryan migration. The Aryans worshiped spirits of plants and animals, and cannabis played an active role in their rituals.

By 1000 B.C., cannabis was commonly used throughout the Indian sub-continent. The plant was used to lower fevers, as a sleep aid, to cure dysentery and most importantly as a means of prolonging life.

A popular medical treatment was bhang, a drink consisting of cannabis and milk that was used as an anesthetic and an anti-phlegmatic.[I]

The first major written reference to the medical use of cannabis was documented in the Ayurvedic, a system of traditional Indian medicine. In its treatise, *Sushruta Samhita*, cannabis is referenced as a cure for leprosy and as an anti-phlegmatic.[II]

The *Vendidad*, an ancient Persian religious text, was written around the seventh century B.C. It was significantly influenced by the *Vedas*, which are the oldest literature in Sanskrit and the key to Hinduism. It mentions bhang and names cannabis as the most important of 10,000 medicinal plants.[11]

Cannabis was also described in the ancient Sanskrit Vedic poem, *Science of Charms* as one of the "five kingdoms of herbs...which release us from anxiety."

[I] Bhang has been used as an intoxicant for centuries in the Indian subcontinent. In India and Nepal it is used during some Hindu festivals and consuming bhang at such occasions was and continues to be a common practice.
[II] Ayurvedic medicine, also known as Ayurveda, was developed thousands of years ago in India. It is one of the world's oldest holistic, or whole-body healing systems. It is based on the belief that health and wellness depend on a delicate balance between the mind, body, and spirit.

When Islam came to India in the 16th century, controversy arose regarding the use of cannabis. Many Muslims opposed its popularity as a psychoactive, based on their interpretation of Sharia law. Despite the conflict, many Muslim doctors recognized cannabis' medical value, and based their recommendations on traditional Indian and Persian medical uses.

The Indian Hemp Commission was formed by the Indian government in 1893 with a mandate to examine the use of the plant. The Commission's report was favorable and acknowledged the benefits of cannabis for many diseases and medical conditions. These included the plant's use as an analgesic, a restorer of energy, to control bleeding, a substance to induce contractions, an antidiuretic, and as an aid in treating hay fever, cholera, dysentery, gonorrhea, diabetes, impotence, urinary incontinence, swelling of the testicles, open sores, and chronic ulcers. The report also outlined other benefits, including the prevention of insomnia, reduction in anxiety, protection against cholera, and as an aid to alleviate hunger and to enhance concentration.[12]

The Commission's report was formerly adopted in 1903, with the publication of the medical treatise, the *Materia Medica of India and Their Therapeutics*. The Treatise endorsed cannabis as a treatment for various diseases including asthma, bronchitis and as a treatment for the loss of appetite.[13]

The Use of Cannabis by the Ancient Greeks and Romans

The use of cannabis was prevalent throughout the ancient Greek and Roman empires. Around approximately 200 B.C., it was used in Greece as a medicine for edema or swelling, inflammation, and earaches.

During the time-span of approximately 40 to 90 A.D., the Greek physician, Pedanius Dioscorides traveled on Roman military campaigns as a doctor. During his travels, Dioscorides studied plants and their medical uses. Between 50 and 70 A.D., Dioscorides authored *De Materia Medica*, which translates as "*On Medical Material.*" *De Materia Medica*, which became an important medical text for the next 1500 years, referenced both female and male cannabis plants.[1] Dioscorides wrote that cannabis was useful in making rope, and he also described the plant as containing a liquid that was beneficial in treating earaches and for suppressing sexual urges.[14]

In approximately 79 A.D., Pliny the Elder indicated that the roots of the cannabis plant boiled in water eased cramped joints, provided benefit for gout and "similar violent pain."

---

[1] Latin for "On Medical Material" the text is a five volume encyclopedia and pharmacopeia of herbs and their medicinal use. It includes approximately 600 plants, some animal and mineral substances, and around 1000 plant-derived medicines.

JEFFREY FRIEDLAND

Chapter 8: Cannabis in Europe

The Scythians, a nomadic Eurasian tribe, brought cannabis across the Altai Mountains into Germany in the fifth century A.D. Around the same time, Anglo-Saxon invaders brought it to the British Isles.

The use of cannabis spread throughout Europe during the Middle Ages. Cannabis-based medicine was commonly used for a variety of ailments, including toothaches and to relieve pain during childbirth.

In 1538, William Turner, who is credited as being the first English botanist, praised the benefits of cannabis in his *A New Herball*.[1]

Robert Burton, in 1621, an Oxford scholar and English Clergyman, recommended the plant as a treatment for depression in *The Anatomy of Melancholy*.[15]

The British herbalist Nicholas Culpeper wrote in 1652, in *The English Physitian*, that a hemp extract:

---

[1] *A New Herball* was originally published during the second half of the sixteenth century. It was the first English treatise on herbs and plants that claimed to be based on science.

"allayeth inflammations in the head ... eases the pains of the gout ... knots in the joynts, [and] the pains of the sinews and hips."

The Father of Medical Cannabis

Dr. William O'Shaughnessy, a British army surgeon, is considered by many to be the father of modern cannabis medicine. O'Shaughnessy joined the British East India Company in 1833 and started his career treating soldiers who returned to England from India, many of whom suffered from cholera. His treatment of these soldiers led to his development of intravenous therapy.

O'Shaughnessy was one of the founders of the Calcutta Medical College and Hospital, where he was a professor. While in India, he became familiar with traditional Ayurvedic and Islamic medicine and conducted experiments on a variety of Indian medicinal plants, including opium and cannabis. His research substantiated many of the traditional uses of cannabis and led to discoveries of new medical uses for the plant. His research culminated in writing the first English text on Indian medicinal plants, the *Memoranda on India Materia Medica*, which was presented to the Royal Society in 1838.[16]

O'Shaughnessy's research further popularized the use of cannabis-based medicine in England. One of his most famous successes was the ending of muscle spasms caused by tetanus and rabies with a cannabis extract. O'Shaughnessy's extract did not cure tetanus, but it reduced the symptoms.[17]

He observed that a cannabis extract reduced symptoms of spasticity and suffering as well as relieving the pain of rheumatism and calmed the convulsions of infants.[1] These infant convulsions may have been Dravet syndrome, a form of epilepsy, which was shown to be responsive to a high-CBD strain of cannabis, Charlotte's Web, 175 years later.

---

[1] Spasticity refers to feelings of stiffness and a wide range of involuntary muscle spasms, sustained muscle contractions or sudden movements. Spasticity may be as mild as the feeling of tightness of muscles or it may be so severe as to produce painful, uncontrollable spasms of extremities, usually of the legs.

Chapter 9: The Arrival of Cannabis in Latin America

Columbus' discovery of the Americas in 1492 ushered in a massive two-way transfer of plants and animals between the Eastern and Western hemispheres. Cannabis was one of the first plants brought to the Americas by European explorers and settlers.

The first users of cannabis in Latin America were not the indigenous population, but European settlers. The native population had other remedies. The use of cannabis for recreational purposes had strong competition from other psychoactive plants that were indigenous, and that were integrated into local social and cultural practices, including peyote, ololiuhqui, and cocoa leaves.

Slaves and sailors were likely the first in the Americas to smoke cannabis. Many historians have hypothesized that the smoking of cannabis by slaves, both for recreational purposes and to relieve pain, was prevalent on many Latin American plantations.

It's believed that cannabis arrived in Brazil in the mid-1500s, likely both from Africa and Portugal, where it was known as erva santa, the "holy herb." Its use became predominant in Northeast Brazil.

The cultivation of cannabis in Latin America was insufficient to satisfy the demand for the plant, which led to Spain formally encouraging the cultivation of hemp in its colonies in 1777.

Cannabis was known by various names in Brazil. Some were derived from African languages and included fumo-de-angola, "Angolan smoke," and maconha.

By the late 1800s, cannabis use had spread throughout Brazil, especially to areas where there was a significant Afro-Brazilian population. In Latin America, cannabis became prevalent as part of the expression of Afro-Brazilian culture, often in conjunction with dancing and drumming.

Laws were passed banning the sale or public use of cannabis, including in Rio de Janeiro in 1830, Caxias in 1846, and São Luis in 1866. Historians believe that the banning of cannabis was a move to reduce or eliminate Afro-Brazilian cultural and religious practices.

Queen Carlota Joaquina of Portugal spent the last years of her life exiled in Brazil. The story has been told that while she lay on her deathbed in 1830, she asked her slave, Fellsbino, to bring her an infusion of the fibers of "diamba do Amazonas," so that she could die peacefully.

By the end of the 19th century, the use of cannabis had spread throughout Latin America and the Caribbean, but was most popular in Brazil, Mexico, and the West Indies.

Cannabis flourished in Latin America and thrived in the margins of colonial society. It was used by indigenous and mestizo or mixed-race areas adjacent to towns and villages. In one of these, the Atlixco, Puebla in Mexico, indigenous Indians planted cannabis or pipilzintzintlis as they called the plant and used it for divination purposes.

After the abolition of slavery in the British-ruled Caribbean colonies, indentured workers were imported from India to replace

African slaves on sugar plantations. Most came from the Bengal region of India, where one of India's largest cannabis fields, the 60,000-acre Ganja Mahal flourished in the 19th century. These Bengalis, along with Afro-Caribbeans called the plant ganja, a name that would remain popular for the plant in Jamaica and many other Caribbean islands.

On many islands in the Caribbean, the use of cannabis for its psychoactive properties became the main and significantly less expensive alternative to the local sugar-cane derived rum.

JEFFREY FRIEDLAND

Chapter 10: Cannabis Comes to North America

"Make the most of the Indian hemp seed and sow it everywhere."

George Washington

Cannabis was first brought to North America in 1611 by the English colonists who settled Jamestown. They referred to the plant as hemp. The Jamestown settlement was sponsored by the Virginia Company of London. In exchange for funding the journey, the settlers agreed to work for the Virginia Company, which managed the settlment, its land, and resources.

By 1619, every colonist was ordered by the Virginia Company to provide 100 hemp plants for export to England. Over the next several years, similar decrees were instituted in other colonies.

In 1682, Virginia encouraged hemp production by making it legal tender for as much as one-fourth of a farmer's debts. Maryland enacted similar laws in 1683, followed by Pennsylvania in 1706. Hemp became a form of legal tender in much of the American colonies, and later in many U.S. states, from 1631 until the early 1800s.[18]

The growing of hemp flourished throughout the mid-1800s when imports of hemp and other crops began to replace American grown hemp. But, America's hemp also had other properties. It was increasingly used for recreation and as medicine.

In 1850, cannabis became listed in the *Pharmacopeia of the United States of America* under "Extractum Cannabis, an alcohol extract of the dried tops of Cannabis Sativa, variety Indica." The Pharmacopoeia listed cannabis as a treatment for a variety of ailments, including pain, tetanus, typhus, cholera, rabies, dysentery, alcoholism, opiate addiction, anthrax, leprosy, incontinence, gout, convulsive disorders, tonsillitis, insanity, excessive menstrual bleeding, and uterine bleeding. This inclusion in the Pharmacopeia led to cannabis became an increasingly popular ingredient in many medicinal products.

The inclusion of cannabis in the Pharmacopeia led to numerous medical cannabis tinctures being available to American consumers. Cannabis would continue to be included in the Pharmacopeia as a medicine until 1942.[19]

Cannabis became a common ingredient in the salves and elixirs sold in rural areas by traveling salesman. Referred to as "patent medicines," these formulations were marketed for their "secret" ingredients; often high amounts of narcotics, including cannabis, cocaine, and opium.[1] Some of the more popular products contained fifty percent morphine, making them not only dangerous but addictive.

Products such as Piso's Cure, which was later named Piso's Remedy, were produced starting in about 1869. The products' "secret" ingredients varied over the years and included cannabis indica, morphine, opium, and alcohol. They were sold in pharmacies and were at various times marketed as cures for a

---

[1] The term "patent medicine" was associated with drug compounds in the 18th and 19th centuries, often sold with colorful names and even more colorful claims. Today we refer to similar products as over-the-counter medicine.

variety of conditions including consumption and as cough medicine.

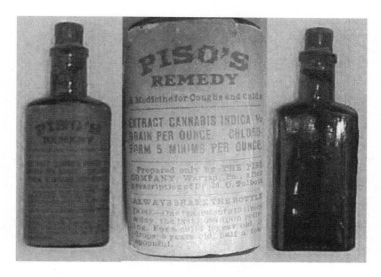

During the final decades of the 18th century, cannabis gained popularity with recreational users. Around 1880, hashish parlors were found in every major city on the East Coast. An article in *Harper's Magazine* in 1883 described a hashish-house in New York frequented by a large clientele, including males and females of "the better classes." It further discussed parlors in Boston, Philadelphia, and Chicago. The article estimated that there were around 500 such establishments in New York City alone.[20]

In 1889, Dr. E. A. Birch wrote an article in the medical journal, *The Lancet*. It described the application of cannabis for the treatment of opium and chloral hydrate withdrawal symptoms.[1] Birch stated that a cannabis-based mixture reduced the craving for opium and acted as a drug that was effective "against vomiting and nausea."[21]

---

[1] *The Lancet* was first published in 1823 and became one of the world's leading medical journals.

JEFFREY FRIEDLAND

Chapter 11: The 1900s, The Movement to Ban Marijuana in the U.S.

"I think people need to be educated to the fact that marijuana is not a drug. Marijuana is an herb and a flower. God put it here. If He put it here and He wants it to grow, what gives the government the right to say that God is wrong?"

Willie Nelson

Cannabis was grown, processed and traded, and recognized for its medicinal, recreational and commercial uses for thousands of years. Starting around the turn of the 20th century, everything began changing in the United States.

The modern American history of cannabis reads like a suspense novel, combining science, profit, and politics, with a cast of characters, some with questionable motives. The plant became subject to confusion, propaganda, deception, and double-crossing from Washington to Hollywood.

The 20th century was ripe with circumstances that paved the way for a movement to ban cannabis in the United States.

Concerns about the therapeutic value and safety of cannabis-based medicine arose at the beginning of the 20th century. Legislation was enacted on a state-by-state basis creating penalties

53

for mislabeling drugs, adulterating them with undisclosed narcotics, and improper sale of those considered "poisons."

These so-called poison laws generally required labels on the packaging indicating the harmful effects of the drugs and also typically limited their purchase to licensed pharmacies. A 1905 bulletin from the U.S. Department of Agriculture listed 29 states with laws mentioning cannabis, eight of which included "sale of poisons" laws that specifically mentioned the plant.

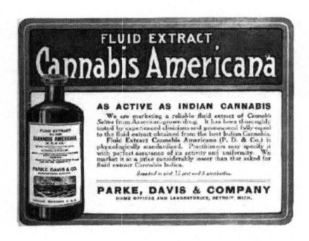

Each state's different regulations created an unwieldy regulatory regime for manufacturers of all patent medicines. In 1906, President Theodore Roosevelt signed the Food and Drugs Act, which became known as the Wiley Act. Its goal was to establish uniform regulations throughout the United States. The law did not address the medical value of given ingredients but established regulations for the products' packaging.[22] The Act stated:

> ...*an article shall also be deemed to be misbranded... if the package fail to bear a statement on the label of the quantity or proportion of any alcohol, morphine, opium, cocaine, heroin, alpha or beta eucaine, chloroform, cannabis indica, chloral hydrate, or acetanilide, or any derivative or preparation of any such substances contained therein.*[23]

The influx of Mexican immigrants fleeing the Mexican Revolution of 1910 fueled the problem. Farmers increased their use of Mexican immigrants as laborers. As unemployment rose, tensions grew between Americans who began to blame immigrants for stealing jobs. Immigrant labor was soon linked to the recreational use of cannabis since it was common for Mexican workers to smoke "marihuana" to relax after a day of working in the fields. This recreational use of cannabis was a new concept for most Anglo-Americans, who were not familiar with the recreational substance's name, marihuana.

Americans looked for a scapegoat to blame for the high rates of unemployment. Mexican immigrants became easy targets. The campaign against cannabis began referring to the plant as "marijuana," because anti-cannabis factions wanted to underscore the drug's "Mexican-ness." The word itself was meant to play off of the anti-immigrant sentiment. The "marijuana menace" then became the battleground between a delineated "us" and "them," which was later expanded to African-Americans, jazz musicians, prostitutes, and "lower-class" whites.

Stories of Mexicans who smoked marijuana, gained superhuman strength and turned into crazed murderers were abundant. Despite these stated facts being untrue, the stereotypes would last for decades.

The passage of the early laws banning marijuana is often described as the result of racism against Mexican Americans. Yet the use of hashish by immigrants from the Middle East was also cited in the push for legislative action.

In 1915, El Paso, Texas became the first U.S. city to ban marijuana. Mexican immigrants who smoked marijuana were rounded up and deported.[24]

The second decade of the 20th century brought with it an increased popular sentiment for prohibiting alcohol in the United States. At the time, legislation seeking to address moral issues including prostitution, racetrack gambling, prizefighting, liquor, and oral sex was popular. Cannabis was a minor afterthought.

Until World War I, cannabis for medicinal purposes was primarily imported from India. This was because the *Pharmacopoeia of the United States*, specified that medical cannabis was from the flowers of the Indian variety of cannabis, "cannabis indica."

World War I interrupted the foreign supply of cannabis for medicine. The lack of availability of foreign cannabis drove the U.S. to become self-sufficient in the production of cannabis for medicine.

After World War I, public resentment and fear of immigrants increased. This escalated public and governmental concerns regarding the recreational use of cannabis.

Cannabis in the 1920s

> *"It really puzzles me to see marijuana connected with narcotics, dope and all that crap. It's a thousand times better than whiskey. It's an assistant, a friend."*
>
> *Louis Armstrong*

The League of Nations sponsored the Second Opium Conference in 1925. The Conference resulted in the adoption of the International Opium Convention.[I] Egypt proposed that cannabis resin, commonly referred to as hashish, be added to the list of narcotics covered by the convention.[II] The convention authorized the use of "Indian hemp" only for scientific and medical purposes and established restrictions on importing and exporting hashish. This League of Nations Convention was the first international treaty to regulate cannabis.[25]

[I] The League of Nations was an intergovernmental organization founded in 1920 after World War I, as the first international organization whose principal mission was to maintain world peace. It lasted for 26 years.
[II] The word hashish derives from "hassassins," members of a medieval Islamic sect, which gained notoriety as assassins and who were reported to have been heavy users of cannabis.

Marijuana, as the plant was beginning to be known, became increasingly popular with musicians and entertainers during the roaring 20s. The surging popularity of the drug among the young and the "hip" of the day frightened and enraged many in the establishment.

It did not help that the use of marijuana increased at approximately the same time that the unemployment rate was headed upwards, toward 25 percent. America's economic problems sparked fear and paranoia in many individuals. Among those who detested marijuana was the powerful William Randolph Hearst.

America's working class was looking for a scapegoat and Hearst, who owned a publishing empire, was ready to give them one. He owned 28 newspapers throughout the United States, including his flagship newspaper, the *San Francisco Examiner*. His holdings also included the *Los Angeles Examiner*, the *Boston American*, and the *Washington Herald*. Hearst owneds magazines included *Cosmopolitan, Town and Country, Harper's Bazaar* and *Good Housekeeping*.

Notorious for his hatred of minorities, Hearst took every opportunity to use his newspapers and magazines to aggravate racial tensions. Hearst especially detested Mexicans and Mexican-Americans, regularly portraying them as lazy, degenerate, and violent, as marijuana smokers and job "stealers." In January 1923, the San Francisco Examiner featured a story that included:

> *Marihuana is a short cut to the insane asylum. Smoke marihuana cigarettes for a month and what was once your brain will be nothing but a storehouse for horrid specters. Hasheesh makes a murderer who kills for the love of killing out of the mildest mannered man...*

Hearst's sought to influence the American public's perception of marijuana by leveraging racism and the common prejudice against Mexican-Americans.

There is evidence that Hearst's financial interests in the lumber and paper industries fueled his desire to not only ban marijuana but more importantly, hemp. Hemp was a substitute for paper made from timber.[26] Approximately 800,000 acres of prime timberland in Mexico owned by Hearst were seized by the rebel Pancho Villa.[27] Hearst's motivation for his racist rants may have been partially influenced by his desire for retaliation against Mexico and Mexican Americans.

Regardless of his motives, Hearst became a major force in the movement to ban marijuana. He initiated an orchestrated campaign against the plant. His newspapers and magazines regularly published sensational stories linking violent crimes to the use of marijuana.

By 1930, the popularization of the Mexican Spanish word "marihuana" was increasingly part of a strategy to ban the cannabis plant. The Federal Bureau of Narcotics starting using "marihuana," and the word began to appear in newspapers and magazines. Neither the words marihuana nor marijuana were included in dictionaries at the time and the words were not familiar to most U.S. citizens. The use of the word marijuana was key to a strategy to differentiate the plant from the American public's familiarity with the agricultural crop, hemp and cannabis medicine.

Without this campaign to outlaw marijuana, it's likely that the plant would still be referred to as cannabis in the United States, as it continues to be known today, in most of the world.

The consumption of alcohol in the United States was pervasive, while marijuana, as a recreational substance, was only used by a small portion of the population. Compared to the difficult campaign to ban alcohol, culminating in Prohibition in 1919, the campaign to ban marijuana was easy.

Newspapers, including tabloids and magazines, began a campaign targeting marijuana. The focus of the tirade against the plant was based mainly on racist ideologies. The initial targets were Mexican immigrants. The implication was that the use of marijuana would incite violent behavior, lead to insanity, addiction, and drug abuse, and even spur some to commit sex crimes.

Reacting to the corruption and scandals that gripped prohibition and narcotics agencies, in 1930 the Federal Bureau of

Narcotics (FBN) was established under the Department of the Treasury. Harry Anslinger was appointed as its first commissioner, a post he retained until 1962. Before his appointment, Anslinger had been an assistant commissioner in the United States Bureau of Prohibition. He was a staunch supporter of the marijuana prohibition movement and the criminalization of drugs. In addition to his objective of banning marijuana federally, Anslinger sought to criminalize marijuana in all states.

Anslinger's appointment did raise a few eyebrows. The decision to nominate Anslinger was strongly influenced by the Treasury Secretary, Andrew Mellon, who was Anslinger's wife's uncle. Mellon was a co-founder of Mellon National Bank, and one of the wealthiest men in America. Mellon had a significant financial interest in the production of nylon, a synthetic replacement for many of the commercial uses of hemp.

By 1931, U.S. government research determined that marijuana was linked to heinous criminal activity "primarily committed by racially inferior or underclass communities," By 1931, 29 states had outlawed marijuana. In 1932, the Uniform State Narcotic Act handed legislative control of marijuana from the Federal Government to the states.

Anslinger believed that marijuana caused insanity and that its users engaged in horrendous acts of criminality. He joined forces with Hearst, and together they embarked on one of the world's most effective and long-lasting smear campaigns.

Hearst and Anslinger were the driving forces responsible for the almost eighty-year illegal status of marijuana. Together they propelled what had been a state-by-state movement to into a national crusade to criminalize the plant.[28]

Racism was the primary tactic that fueled Anslinger's and Hearst's success. They used it as a tactic at every opportunity to leverage America's growing atmosphere of fear and paranoia, by pointing the finger at Mexican immigrants and African-Americans and their use of marijuana.

The first element of Hearst's and Anslinger's campaign was building the association between immigrants and marijuana. Hearst banned the words cannabis and hemp from his newspapers and insisted on using the word marijuana in their place. Carefully-crafted, mostly fictional stories were published, frequently, in the Hearst-owned publications, using the word marijuana in conjunction with Mexican immigrants and their abhorrent behavior.

The Anslinger and Hearst team also instigated a flurry of research linking marijuana use with violence, crime, and other socially deviant behaviors, primarily committed by "racially inferior" or underclass communities.

Reading the articles that appeared in the Hearst and other publications today may seem humorous, but as part of the sensational tabloid-style journalism of the 1930s, they were generally believed. Newspaper headlines such as "While under the influence of marijuana, the individual grabbed a meat cleaver and chopped that poor man's head off," certainly garnered the attention of Americans.

These provocative and inflammatory statements were designed to incense the American public, and they accomplished that objective. Racism was blatant. Often phrases like, "Reefer makes darkies think they're as good as white men," were used to incense the American public.

As the Great Depression deepened and massive unemployment increased, public resentment and fear of Mexican immigrants and other minorities escalated. The public's increased concern created pressure on the U.S. government to further rein in marijuana. The Federal Bureau of Narcotics encouraged state governments to take responsibility for the problem by adopting the Uniform State Narcotic Act in 1932. The Act's objective was to ensure that narcotic drugs had the same safeguards and regulations in all states.

Anslinger continued his smear campaign against Marijuana throughout the 1930s. He ordered Bureau of Narcotics' field agents to gather quotes from police reports depicting the most hideous and depraved criminal and sexual acts imaginable, all indicated as having been committed while under the influence of marijuana. These stories became known as the "Gore File" and quickly became a regular feature in the *American Magazine*.[1]. Anslinger encouraged this practice of publishing creative marijuana stories, and it continued well into the 1970s, long after he was out of office.

Influenced by the mania created by Anslinger and Hearst, and the Gore Files, all 48 U.S. states enacted laws to regulate marijuana and 46 states had passed laws banning the plant's use by 1937.

Anslinger also lobbied the motion picture industry to use films to portray his message about the drug culture. To ratchet-up the rhetoric for his anti-marijuana campaign, Anslinger added movie stars as targets. Actor Robert Mitchum, drummer Gene Krupa, and many other celebrities were arrested for marijuana use, and their arrests were highly publicized.

Reacting to the government attacks, major Hollywood studios essentially handed editorial control of their films to Anslinger, who ensured that they did not include any positive messages about marijuana use.

Financed by a small church group, the movie *Tell Your Children* was produced with the objective of instilling fear of the evils of marijuana in parents. It told the story of marijuana addiction ruining the life of its young leading character. Many of the film's other characters were killed, sexually compromised or committed to lunatic asylums. After its production, the film was purchased by Dwain Esper, an American director, and producer of exploitation films.[II]

[I] The original title, Frank Leslie's Popular Monthly, was first published in 1876. It was renamed Leslie's Monthly Magazine in 1904, and then Leslie's Magazine in 1905. In 1906 it was renamed the American Illustrated Magazine; later shortened to The American Magazine. Its publication ceased in 1956.
[II] Exploitation films were generally low budget, and sought to gain financial success by "exploiting" a niche genre, or featuring a lurid subject matter.

Esper added lewd shots to the film, changed the title to *Reefer Madness* and then released it on the motion picture exploitation circuit in 1936.[29] Despite its misleading plot and cheap effects, *Reefer Madness* proved to be an effective propaganda tool in

highlighting the harmful effects marijuana had on its users. It furthered the alleged connection between marijuana and violent crime.

The Marihuana Tax Act of 1937

Anslinger authored the Marihuana Tax Act of 1937.[1] It was the Federal Government's first attempt to regulate marijuana. The Act effectively criminalized marijuana, restricting the possession

---

[1] In the 1930s, "marihuana" was the spelling most commonly used in U.S. government documents. The Act is now commonly referred to, using the now conventional American spelling, as the Marijuana Tax Act of 1937.

of the plant or products derived from the plant, to individuals who paid an excise tax for specific authorized medical or commercial uses.

Before the Act, the federal government lacked the authority under the U.S. Constitution to regulate medicine. This was a power that was relegated to the states. The decision was made that a tax was the only viable way to criminalize marijuana. While excluding medical and commercial uses, the Act effectively made possession or transfer of marijuana illegal throughout the United States, by imposing an excise tax on all sales of cannabis.

Congress, known for holding months and months of hearings on a single piece of legislation, spent just two hours on the Act. The primary witness was Anslinger, who testified that "Marijuana was an addictive drug which produces in its users insanity, criminality, and death."

Representatives of the Sherman Williams Paint Co. raised concerns regarding the use of hemp since most paints and varnishes were made from hemp seed oil. The Sherman Williams representatives indicated that the company alone used more than 58,000 tons of hemp seeds in 1935.

One of the staunchest opponents to the Act was Dr. William C. Woodward, the legislative counsel of the American Medical Association (AMA). The AMA opposed the Act because it imposed a tax on the physicians who prescribed cannabis, retail pharmacists who sold cannabis, and the cultivation and manufacturing of cannabis, rather than on the end user. Although the AMA's primary opposition to the bill was based on the tax burden, Woodward also sought to make clear that scientific evidence of the medical benefits of cannabis were as yet unknown, but that the plant might well have important uses in medicine and psychology:

> *There is nothing in the medicinal use of Cannabis that has any relation to Cannabis addiction. I use the word 'cannabis' in preference to the word 'marihuana', because Cannabis is the correct term for describing the plant and its products. The term 'marihuana' is a mongrel word that has crept into this*

country over the Mexican border and has no general meaning, except as it relates to the use of Cannabis preparations for smoking.

To say, however, as has been proposed here, that the use of the drug should be prevented by a prohibitive tax, loses sight of the fact that future investigation may show that there are substantial medical uses for Cannabis.[30]

Woodward also voiced concerns about the ties between marijuana addiction, violence, and overdosage. He asserted that because the word marijuana was largely unknown at the time, the medical profession did not realize they were losing their "cannabis medicine."

After the hearings, the U.S. House of Representatives spent less than two minutes in debate before voting to pass the Act into law. There was no debate in the Senate before its vote.

In 1937, President Franklin Roosevelt signed The Marihuana Tax Act of 1937, which required a government stamp to sell or distribute marijuana. In theory, it was just another tax. While not banning the medical use of marijuana it instead required physicians and pharmacists who prescribed or dispensed it to register with federal authorities and pay an annual tax or license fee. However, the government refused to issue any stamps, effectively outlawing the plant. While the Act did not directly ban marijuana, the actual result was the same.[31]

After the passage of the Act, prescriptions of cannabis-based medicine came to a halt. The Act set the stage for the drug war of the following decades. It led to the establishment of an active black market for marijuana, and the prosecution and incarceration of millions of Americans for growing, selling or using the plant.

The final blow was the removal of cannabis from the *U.S. Pharmacopeia* in 1942. This resulted in the plant losing all medical legitimacy in the United States.[32]

The La Guardia Report: Claims About the Dangers of Marijuana Are Unfounded

New York's Mayor, Fiorello LaGuardia, was such a strong opponent of the Marijuana Tax Act, that he requested that the New York Academy of Medicine conduct an investigation of marijuana.[1] The Academy's results were published in the 1944 report, *The Marihuana Problem in the City of New York*, which became known as the *LaGuardia Report*. The Report stated that many claims about the dangers of cannabis were exaggerated or untrue:

> *The practice of smoking marihuana does not lead to addiction in the medical sense of the word... The use of marihuana does not lead to morphine or heroin or cocaine addiction and no effort is made to create a market for these narcotics by stimulating the practice of marihuana smoking... Marihuana is not the determining factor in the commission of major crimes... The publicity concerning the catastrophic effects of marihuana smoking in New York City is unfounded.[33]*

LaGuardia publicly advocated legalizing cannabis. Legend has it that after its publication, Anslinger was so incensed, that he destroyed every copy of the report he could locate.

---

[1] Established in 1847, the New York Academy of Medicine, addressed the health challenges facing the world's urban populations through interdisciplinary approaches to policy leadership, innovative research, evaluation, education, and community engagement.

The 1940s and "Hemp for Victory"

While the use of cannabis was criminalized, the fallout of hemp being considered "marijuana," impacted a major agricultural crop. Among its uses, hemp was crucial for producing marine cordage, parachutes, and other military necessities. The Act forced the U.S. to import hemp from the Philippines and elsewhere in Asia. As many Asian nations fell to Japan during World War II, the need for a U.S supply of hemp became critical.

To meet wartime needs, President Franklin Roosevelt signed an executive order allowing the emergency growing of hemp for the war effort. The Department of Agriculture launched a "Hemp for Victory" campaign, which included a film that stated:

> *...the Navy's rapidly dwindling reserves. When that is gone, American hemp will go on duty again; hemp for mooring ships; hemp for tow lines; hemp for tackle and gear; hemp for countless naval uses both on ship and shore. Just as in the days when Old Ironsides sailed the seas victorious with her hempen shrouds and hempen sails. Hemp for victory!*

Farmers were incentivized to grow industrial hempand were provided with seeds. Draft deferments were provided to those who would stay home and grow hemp. The program also provided tax stamps to farmers to facilitate compliance with the Marihuana Tax Act of 1937.

In 1943, American farmers harvested 375,000 acres of hemp for the war effort. Two years later, when World War II ended, the Roosevelt administration reinstituted its ban on hemp production. Facing stiff federal penalties, industrial hemp farmers plowed under their hemp crops.

Chapter 12: Marijuana in the Second Half of the 20th Century

"They've outlawed the number-one vegetable on the planet."

Timothy Leary

In 1951, President Harry Truman signed into law the Boggs Act. The Act mandated minimum prison sentences for drug-related crimes, including two-to-five year minimum sentences for first offenses, including possession.[1] The Boggs Act was based on a popular belief that drug addiction was contagious, that it was likely an incurable disease, and that addicts should be quarantined and forced to undergo treatment. For purposes of sentencing, the Boggs Act made no distinction between drug traffickers and users.[34]

Within three days of the Boggs Act becoming law on January 1, 1952, over 500 people were arrested for drug-related offenses.

Four years later, the Narcotics Control Act of 1956 was signed into law. The Act quantified marijuana as a narcotic, which set stricter mandatory sentences for marijuana-related offenses. A

---

[1] Named for its sponsor, Representative Hale Boggs of Louisiana.

67

first offense for marijuana possession carried a minimum sentence of two to ten years, with a fine of up to $20,000.

Marijuana in the 1960s

The election of John Kennedy ushered in a changed political and cultural climate. Kennedy's presidency highlighted conflicting cultural views, which were frequently attributed to a growing generation gap. The formative years of what became known as the baby boom generation ushered in transformational social changes which led to significant contrasts. These included flower children and assassinations, the Vietnam War and the Peace Corp, the civil rights movement and the walk on the moon.

The 1960s also began an era of the increasing use of marijuana by America's Anglo middle and upper-middle classes. As marijuana use became widespread among Anglo college students, many attitudes regarding marijuana and drug policy started to change.

One of Anslinger's final undertakings before leaving government service in 1962 was his lobbying to promote his agenda internationally. In 1961, the United Nations Office of Drugs and Crime adopted the *Single Convention on Narcotic Drugs*. The Convention sought to prohibit the production and supply of narcotics and similar drugs for purposes other than medicine and research, and categorized drugs into schedules, from the most dangerous to the least dangerous.

While earlier international treaties sought to control opium and coca, as well as their derivatives such as morphine, heroin, and cocaine; the Convention was broadened to include cannabis. Anslinger's lobbying resulted in cannabis being placed under Schedule I, the Convention's most stringent regulatory regime.

A Canadian Senate committee report noted:

At the U.S.'s insistence, cannabis was placed under the heaviest control regime in the Convention, Schedule IV. The argument for placing cannabis in this category was that it was widely abused. The World Health Organization later found that cannabis could have medical applications after all, but the structure was already in place and no international action has since been taken to correct this anomaly.[35]

All countries who became signatories to the Convention were required to establish the necessary infrastructure to implement and comply with its regulations.

The U.S. Senate approved the Convention in 1967. The National Institute on Drug Abuse (NIDA) was then established to provide the oversight and compliance functions mandated by the Convention, responsibilities NIDA continues to provide today.

A key provision of the Convention prohibited anyone other than governments from growing cannabis. NIDA contracted with the University of Mississippi to grow cannabis for the U.S. government. This Mississippi-grown cannabis became the sole legal source for all U.S. research and medical needs. NIDA also contracted with the Research Triangle Institute to manufacture and distribute cigarettes produced from marijuana grown by the University.[36]

Ironically, the Convention's language regarding the criminalization of the possession of drugs for personal use was somewhat ambiguous. And in the decades that followed, it was this ambiguity that provided the legal basis for individual states to legalize possession of marijuana for personal use.

Marijuana consumption continued to gain popularity, most notably on college campuses. This was intensified by a growing number of Americans questioning earlier assertions regarding the dangerous effects of the plant. Fueling this change in sentiment, reports commissioned by Presidents Kennedy and Johnson found that the use of marijuana did not induce violence nor did it lead to the use of stronger drugs.

Significant increases in the consumption of illicit drugs across the country energized the legislative tug-of-war and led President Lyndon Johnson to implement Reorganization Plan No. 1 in 1968. This Plan combined the Federal Bureau of Narcotics and the Bureau of Drug Abuse Control to form the Bureau of Narcotics and Dangerous Drugs (BNDD), which was established under the Department of Justice.[37] The BNDD became America's primary narcotics law enforcement agency.

The 1960s ended with a ruling by the Supreme Court in the case of Leary v. United States.[38] Timothy Leary, a noted professor, and activist was arrested for the possession of marijuana in violation of the Marihuana Tax Act. Leary challenged the act on the ground that compliance required self-incrimination, thereby violating his Fifth Amendment rights. The court unanimously agreed, declaring the Act unconstitutional and Leary's conviction was overturned.

Cannabis in the 1970s

After the Leary Supreme Court decision, many states began abolishing their laws banning the possession or sale of marijuana. Congress also repealed most of the mandatory penalties for drug-related offenses, viewing them as overly harsh and having had minimal impact on eliminating the use of illegal drugs.

In response to the Leary judgment, Congress established the Comprehensive Drug Abuse Prevention and Control Act of 1970. It repealed the Marihuana Tax Act of 1937 and established the Controlled Substances Act (CSA) as the new foundation for the continued fight against drug abuse. The CSA consolidated existing laws regulating the manufacture and distribution of narcotics, stimulants, depressants, hallucinogens, anabolic and other chemicals used in the illicit production of controlled substances.

Similar to the Single Convention on Narcotic Drugs, the CSA classified narcotic substances into schedules, with Schedule I substances being the most hazardous and Schedule V the most benign. The Assistant Secretary for Health and Scientific Affairs of the Department of Health, Education and Welfare, Roger Egeberg, indicated to Congress:

...Some question has been raised whether the use of the plant itself produces 'severe psychological or physical dependence' as required by a schedule I or even schedule II criterion. Since there is still a considerable void in our knowledge of the plant and effects of the active drug contained in it, our recommendation is that marihuana be retained within schedule I at least until the completion of certain studies now underway to resolve the issue. If those studies make it appropriate for the Attorney General to change the placement of marihuana to a different schedule, he may do so in accordance with the authority provided under section 201 of the bill.

Marijuana was placed in Schedule I, the most restrictive category of drugs, which also included heroin, LSD, and cocaine. The CSA indicated that marijuana was:

> ...*classified as having a high potential for abuse, no currently accepted medical use in treatment in the United States, and a lack of accepted safety for use of the drug or other substance under medical supervision.*[39]

The CSA also required the creation of a bipartisan National Commission on Marijuana and Drug Abuse (NCMDA). The principal objective of NCMDA was to evaluate marijuana laws to determine whether or not the plant should be decriminalized. President Richard Nixon appointed Raymond Shafer as its commissioner.

The Shafer Commission Report and President Nixon's Response

In 1972, the National Commission on Marijuana and Drug Abuse, which became known as the Shafer Commission, concluded its study. The Commission concluded that marijuana should be decriminalized, but that public use and driving while intoxicated should remain illegal.

Shafer presented the Commission's report to Congress, which was entitled, *Marihuana, A Signal of Misunderstanding*. The report recommended ending the prohibition of marijuana.[40] Later that year the commission issued its comprehensive, 480-page report, *Drug Use in America: Problem in Perspective*.[41] The report stated:

71

...decades before, 'the absence of adequate understanding of the effects of the drug combined with "lurid accounts of [largely unsubstantiated] "marijuana atrocities" greatly affected public opinion and labeled the stereotypical user as physically aggressive, lacking in self-control, irresponsible, mentally ill and, perhaps most alarming, criminally inclined and dangerous.

The report recommended that possession of marijuana in public, and distribution of larger quantities should be punishable by a fine. It also concluded that driving under the influence and disorderly conduct should be punishable by jail time and a fine, similar to laws regarding the use of alcohol.

The report recommended that marijuana used for personal purposes should no longer be considered an offense. Public use of marijuana would remain illegal and subject to seizure and forfeiture. Casual distribution of small amounts of marijuana for minimal or no compensation, and without the objective of generating a profit would not be an offense.[42] The report also stated:

Recognizing the use of drugs for pleasure or other non-medical purposes is not inherently irresponsible; alcohol is widely used as an acceptable part of social activities.

The report predicted the failure of the War on Drugs that President Richard Nixon had declared in 1971, a year earlier. It recommended the implementation of:

...a social control policy seeking to discourage marijuana use, while concentrating primarily on the prevention of heavy and very heavy use.

The Commission also questioned whether the prohibition of marijuana possession was constitutional. The report indicated that the legislative and executive branches of the government had a responsibility to obey the U.S. Constitution, even without a court ruling requiring them to do so.

The Shafer Commission conclusions met significant resistance. In 1974, a Senate subcommittee hearing led by Senator James Eastland concluded:

...five years of research has provided strong evidence that, if corroborated, would suggest that marijuana in various forms is far more hazardous than originally suspected.

Nixon, a staunch opponent of decriminalization, refused to implement the Shafer Commission recommendations and essentially ignored the report. Addressing his position in a 1971 televised news conference, he stated:

> *As you know, there is a Commission that is supposed to make recommendations to me about this subject; in this instance, however, I have such strong views that I will express them. I am against legalizing marijuana. Even if the Commission does recommend that it be legalized, I will not follow that recommendation... I can see no social or moral justification whatever for legalizing marijuana. I think it would be exactly the wrong step. It would simply encourage more and more of our young people to start down the long, dismal road that leads to hard drugs and eventually self-destruction.[43]*

Nixon's took the position that drug abuse was "America's public enemy number one." In 1973, he launched an all-out offensive. Nixon's "Reorganization Plan Number Two" proposed the creation of a new, single federal agency to enforce federal drug laws. Congress voted Nixon's legislation into law, to a large extent to counter a growing concern of the American public regarding the increasing availability of drugs.

The Reorganization Plan established the Drug Enforcement Administration (DEA). The DEA consolidated the narcotics activities of the Bureau of Narcotics and Dangerous Drugs, the Office of Drug Abuse Law Enforcement, and the drug-related activities of the Bureau of Customs.

Despite the hardline actions taken by Nixon and Congress, during the 1970s eleven states decriminalized marijuana and most others reduced the penalties for possession of small quantities.

Looking back, the recommendations of the Shafer Commission's report have stood the test of time.

Marijuana prohibitionists were dealt another blow in 1976, when Robert Randall, an American glaucoma patient, defended himself against criminal charges of cultivating marijuana. He invoked a defense based on the rarely used Doctrine of Necessity.[1]

---

[1] Defendants seeking to rely on this defense, when their conduct is not allowed

A federal judge agreed and ruled that Randall's use of marijuana constituted a medical necessity. The judge dismissed the criminal charges and ordered the Food and Drug Administration to provide Randall with 300 marijuana cigarettes monthly.

With this ruling, Randall became the first American to receive marijuana legally for the treatment of a medical condition and set the stage for what became known as "compassionate use."[44]

By 1978, the U.S. Department of Health and Human Services supplied marijuana to seven patients whose physicians received approval for Investigational New Drug Applications (IND) from the Food and Drug Administration for compassionate use.[45]

Also in 1978, New Mexico became the first state to acknowledge the medical value of marijuana and passed the Controlled Substances Therapeutic Research Act. Over the next few years, more than 30 states would pass similar legislation.

Marijuana in the 1980s

"I now have absolute proof that smoking even one marijuana cigarette is equal in brain damage to being on Bikini Island during an H-bomb blast"

Ronald Reagan, 40ᵗʰ U.S. President

Ronald Reagan was elected U.S. President in 1980, ushering in a new conservative era. Together with his wife, Nancy, the Reagans revitalized the War on Drugs. The First Lady's famous "Just Say No" campaign was designed to stop children and young adults from falling prey to peer pressure and using illegal drugs.

When Reagan signed the Comprehensive Crime Control Act of 1984, it was the first comprehensive review of the U.S. criminal code in decades. The Act increased penalties for the cultivation, possession or transfer of marijuana.

Supporters of the War on Drugs favored the legislation. Many other Americans did not. The Los Angeles Times stated in

---

under a specific law, argue that they should not be held liable for a crime because their conduct was necessary to prevent some greater harm.

an article, *Forfeiture Law Casts a Shadow on Presumption of Innocence*, that the:

> *Government uses the statute to seize money and property believed to be linked to narcotics trafficking. But critics say it short-circuits the Constitution.*

While the Reagan administration was tightening the regulations on the use of marijuana, the country's National Cancer Institute (NCI) began the experimental distribution of a new drug, Dronabinol, also known by its trade name, Marinol.[1] It was a chemically synthesized, oral form of THC and was initially distributed to cancer patients in San Francisco.

Around the same time, six states conducted studies comparing the benefits of smoking marijuana to the use of Marinol by cancer patients who were undergoing chemotherapy and who had not responded to other anti-nausea medications. These state-sponsored studies concluded that thousands of patients found marijuana more effective than the synthetic Marinol, a conclusion which was contrary to the position of the U.S. government. The Federal Government ignored the states' research conclusions and instead approved the use of Marinol as an anti-nausea medication.

Reagan doubled down on his War on Drugs in 1986 when he signed the Anti-Drug Abuse Act, which instituted mandatory sentences for drug-related crimes. The new law raised federal penalties for marijuana possession and dealing, basing the penalty on the quantity involved in the crime. The Act made the penalty for possession of 100 marijuana plants the same as for possession of 100 grams of heroin. A later amendment to the Act established the "three strikes and you're out" policy, providing life sentences

---

[1] In 1981, the U.S. government sold the patent for Marinol to the pharmaceutical company, Unimed. In 1985, Unimed obtained Food and Drug Administration (FDA) approval and began marketing Marinol for terminal cancer patients in capsule form as a treatment for nausea. In 1992, Marinol was approved by FDA for the treatment of anorexia associated with weight loss in patients with AIDS.

for repeat drug offenders and the death penalty for major drug trafficking and "drug kingpins."[46]

In 1988, Francis Young, an administrative law judge with the Drug Enforcement Administration, was asked by the DEA to respond to a 1972 petition by the National Organization for the Reform of Marijuana Laws (NORML). The petition requested that marijuana be rescheduled under the Controlled Substances Act.[1] Young recommended that marijuana be rescheduled from Schedule I to Schedule II for cancer patients suffering from nausea associated with chemotherapy. He also ruled that there was insufficient evidence to allow patient use of marijuana for pain or glaucoma.

Young's ruling included:

The evidence in this record clearly shows that marijuana has been accepted as capable of relieving the distress of great numbers of very ill people, and doing so with safety under medical supervision. It would be unreasonable, arbitrary and capricious for DEA to continue to stand between those sufferers and the benefits of this substance in light of the evidence in this record.[47]

The Reagan administration's Department of Justice successfully appealed Young's ruling. The appeal affirmed the government's total ban on marijuana, including for sick or dying patients whose physicians recommended its use. Marijuana remained a Schedule I controlled substance.[48]

The War on Drugs gained another supporter in 1989, when President George H.W. Bush swore "the scourge would end," in his first televised speech as president from the Oval Office.

Marijuana in the 1990s

The battle to legalize marijuana for medical use gained momentum during the 1990s.

---

[1] NORML's mission is to "move public opinion sufficiently to legalize the responsible use of marijuana by adults, and to serve as an advocate for consumers to assure they have access to high quality marijuana that is safe, convenient and affordable."

In the spring of 1990, the American Society of Clinical Oncology surveyed its members regarding the use of marijuana for patients undergoing chemotherapy. Forty-four percent of its members indicated that they recommended marijuana to at least one patient, 63 percent indicated that they believed that marijuana was beneficial as a treatment for nausea for patients undergoing chemotherapy, and 53 percent favored marijuana being available by prescription.[49]

In 1991, Florida's First District Court of Appeals ruled on an application based on the Doctrine of Necessity in the case of Jenks v. State of Florida. It ruled for the defendant, concluding that a patient must be suffering from a medically recognized illness or disease, which resulted in symptoms for which marijuana is the only effective treatment.[50]

That same year, Proposition P was passed by 79 percent of voters in San Francisco. The proposition requested that the State of California and the California Medical Association "restore hemp medical preparations to the list of available medicines in California," and not penalize physicians "for prescribing hemp preparations for medical purposes."[51]

Around the same time, the U.S. Department of Health and Human Services (HHS) phased out its compassionate use medical marijuana program, which had provided marijuana to seriously ill patients. The Department based its decision on the program being counter to the government's anti-drug policies. At the time, only six patients were receiving marijuana under the program and they were allowed to continue receiving it. A directive signed by James Mason, chief of the Public Health Service, encouraged patients considering marijuana to instead use the synthetic form of THC, Marinol. Mason said:

> *If it's perceived that the Public Health Service is going around giving marijuana to folks, there would be a perception that this stuff can't be so bad. It gives a bad signal...*

Leading to the HHS decision was the concern that while only six patients had received marijuana under the program, the FDA received 28 applications in the previous year, and that the government would be deluged with hundreds of additional applications, because of the spread of AIDS.[52]

In 1992, Dr. James Mason, the Assistant Secretary of Health and Human services in the Bush Administration, terminated the entire compassionate access program for medical marijuana. He stated that the program was growing too large, too visible, too expensive and was too time-consuming for the FDA to administer. Thirteen patients who had been receiving medical marijuana would be grandfathered in and would continue to be supplied government marijuana. Those patients suffered from AIDS, Glaucoma, Multiple Sclerosis, and other conditions.[53]

Americans on the other side of the War on Drugs kept fighting as well, although they were not as successful as the government. In 1994, in response to a petition submitted 22 years earlier to reschedule marijuana to Schedule II, which would have enabled physicians to legally prescribe it, the U.S. Court of Appeals upheld the Drug Enforcement Administration's decision to keep marijuana in Schedule I.

Two and a half years later, California voters passed Proposition 215 by a 56 percent margin. The proposition allowed patients and their caregivers, with a physician's recommendation, to possess and grow marijuana for the treatment of diseases including cancer, AIDS, muscular spasticity, and migraines. It protected physicians from prosecution for recommending marijuana.[54]

As researchers continued to amass greater understanding of the physical and psychoactive effects of marijuana, regulators faced increasing pressure to reevaluate their stance on the plant's use.

In 1997, America's Drug Czar, General Barry McCaffrey, the Director of the Office of National Drug Control Policy, commissioned the Institute of Medicine of the National Academy of Sciences to review the science regarding the potential health benefits and risks of marijuana and cannabinoids.[1] What resulted was the most rigorous government-sponsored scientific review of medical marijuana to date.

The findings were published in March 1999 in a 257-page report, *Marijuana and Medicine: Assessing the Science Base*. The report emphasized the need for well-formulated, scientific research into the therapeutic effects of marijuana and its cannabinoid components on patients with specific disease conditions.[55] The report included the following statement:

> *The accumulated data indicate a potential therapeutic value for cannabinoid drugs, particularly for symptoms such as pain relief, control of nausea and vomiting, and appetite stimulation. The therapeutic effects of cannabinoids are best established for THC (tetrahydrocannabinol), which is generally 1 of the 2 most abundant of the cannabinoids in marijuana.*

Despite the findings of the Report, marijuana remained a Schedule I substance.

Ironically, in July 1999, Unimed successfully petitioned to have the synthetic THC, Marinol, moved to Schedule III to make the pharmaceutical more widely available to patients. The rescheduling was approved after a review by the DEA and the Department of Health and Human Services, which found little evidence of Marinol's abuse. Marinol's move to Schedule III resulted in fewer regulatory controls and reduced criminal penalties for its illicit use.[56]

The movement to legalize or decriminalize marijuana in the United States gained momentum as the 21st century approached. California became the first state to legalize medical marijuana in 1996 when 56 percent of voters passed a ballot initiative.

Activists also continued the quest to reschedule marijuana in recognition of its medical value. In 1997, the *New England Journal of Medicine* published an editorial calling for marijuana to be

---

[1] Appointed by President Bill Clinton in 1996. General Barry McCaffrey was the fourth director of the Office of National Drug Control Policy. "Drug Czar" was a term first used by in October 1982, by then-Senator Joe Biden.

rescheduled, entitled, *Federal Foolishness and Marijuana*. The editorial stated:

> *Federal authorities should rescind their prohibition of the medicinal use of marijuana for seriously ill patients and allow physicians to decide which patients to treat. The government should change marijuana's status from that of a Schedule I drug (considered to be potentially addictive and with no current medical use) to that of a Schedule II drug (potentially addictive but with some accepted medical use) and regulate it accordingly.*[57]

That same year, the National Institutes of Health convened a group of experts to evaluate the medical value of marijuana. Their conclusion was that scientific evidence was insufficient to definitively assess the therapeutic potential of marijuana, stating, "traditional scientific process should be allowed to evaluate the drug's use for certain disorders."[58]

Many in the medical community concluded that it was beneficial to evaluate the medicinal value of marijuana, but pushback from government agencies continued.

Former American presidents also weighed in on the discussion. In 1998, former Republican presidents Ford and Bush, and Democratic President Carter jointly released a statement before the November elections urging voters to reject state initiatives to legalize medical marijuana. The presidents' joint statement stated that these initiatives: *"circumvented the standard process by which the Food and Drug Administration tested medicine for safety and effectiveness."*[59]

Despite the government efforts and the joint statement by the former presidents, the 1998 initiatives to legalize medical marijuana passed in every state where they were on the ballot. Alaska, Oregon and Washington became the next three states to legalize medical marijuana. Fifty-eight percent of Alaska voters, 55 percent of Oregon voters, and 59 percent of Washington voters approved the initiatives.[60] Maine soon followed.

As the 20th century ended, medical cannabis was legal in five states. These initial state victories hinted at a theme that was going to be prevalent over the next fifteen years. An increasing percentage of Americans favored the legalization of medical marijuana.

Chapter 13: Marijuana in our Century

"40 million American smoked marijuana. The only ones who didn't like it were Judge Ginsberg, Clarence Thomas, and Bill Clinton."

Jay Leno

With the arrival of the 21st century, the state-by-state movement to legalize marijuana gained momentum. Hawaii became the first state to decriminalize marijuana for medical purposes through legislative action rather than by a vote of the people. Colorado and Nevada also passed similar legislation in 2000.

Although it had been slow going, Americans were now increasingly favoring legalizing medical marijuana. Voters continued the push to legalize medical marijuana but the federal government remained steadfast in its position that it provided no medical benefit.

The Schedule I status of marijuana was viewed as hypocritical by many Americans when the U.S. Department of Health and Human Services received a patent in 2003 for the therapeutic use of "cannabinoids as antioxidants and neuroprotectants." The patent abstract stated, "the cannabinoids are found to have particular application as neuroprotectants...in the treatment of neurodegenerative diseases such as Alzheimer's disease."[61]

(12) **United States Patent**
Hampson et al.

(10) Patent No.: **US 6,630,507 B1**
(45) Date of Patent: **Oct. 7, 2003**

(54) **CANNABINOIDS AS ANTIOXIDANTS AND NEUROPROTECTANTS**

(75) Inventors: **Aidan J. Hampson**, Irvine, CA (US); **Julius Axelrod**, Rockville, MD (US); **Maurizio Grimaldi**, Bethesda, MD (US)

(73) Assignee: **The United States of America as represented by the Department of Health and Human Services**, Washington, DC (US)

(*) Notice: Subject to any disclaimer, the term of this

OTHER PUBLICATIONS

Windholz et al., The Merck Index, Tenth Edition (1983) p. 241, abstract No. 1723.*
Mechoulam et al., "A Total Synthesis of d1–Δ¹–Tetrahydrocannabinol, the Active Constituent of Hashish¹," *Journal of the American Chemical Society,* 87:14:3273–3275 (1965).
Mechoulam et al., "Chemical Basis of Hashish Activity," *Science,* 18:611–612 (1970).
Ottersen et al., "The Crystal and Molecular Structure of Cannabidiol," *Acta Chem. Scand. B 31,* 9:807–812 (1977).
Cunha et al., "Chronic Administration of Cannabidiol to Healthy Volunteers and Epileptic Patients¹," *Pharmacology,*

Legalization activists also made headway with older Americans.[62] A 2004 poll by AARP found that 72 percent of seniors supported medical marijuana.[1]

America's regulatory agencies were still unwilling to change course. The conflict between the legality of marijuana at the state and federal levels remained a contentious issue. This became apparent in 2005 when the U.S. Supreme Court ruled that California's 1996 medical marijuana law conflicted with the federal Controlled Substances Act, which banned possession of marijuana.[63]

A year later, in 2006, the Food and Drug Administration confirmed its opposition to marijuana for medical purposes. In a report the FDA stated:

> *There is currently sound evidence that smoked marijuana is harmful. A past evaluation by several Department of Health and Human Services (HHS) agencies... concluded that no sound scientific studies supported medical use of marijuana for treatment in the United States, and no animal or human data supported the safety or efficacy of marijuana for general medical use...:*[64]

The tug-of-war waged on throughout the first decade of the century. In 2008, the U.S.'s second-largest physician group, the

---

[1] AARP was originally named the American Association of Retired Persons, but in 1999 it officially changed its name to "AARP" to reflect a change in focus to reflect a constituency consisting of Americans over 50.

American College of Physicians voiced its support for the legalization of non-smoked forms of THC and research on the benefits of medical marijuana. The College also supported the review of the federal scheduling of marijuana as a Schedule I controlled substance. It also supported the establishment of an exemption from criminal prosecution for physicians who prescribed marijuana.[65]

In 2009, the American Medical Association's revised its position on marijuana. The Association advocated that the status of marijuana as a Schedule I controlled substance be reviewed with the:

"goal of facilitating the conduct of clinical research and development of cannabinoid-based medicines, and alternate delivery methods."[66]

When the first decade of the 21st century came to a close, 13 states had approved the medical use of marijuana, and more state approvals were on their way.

Marijuana in the Second Decade of the 21st Century

By 2010, 15 states and the District of Columbia had enacted laws legalizing medical marijuana.

In March 2011, citing "the dangers of marijuana and the lack of clinical research supporting its medicinal value," the American Society of Addiction Medicine (ASAM) issued a white paper recommending a halt to marijuana medicine in the states where it was legal under state law.

In 2011, in a further push-back by the Federal government, the DEA denied a nine-year-old request from 2002, that marijuana should be reclassified from Schedule I. In its ruling, the DEA once-again took the position that marijuana has "no accepted medical use."

While efforts to reschedule marijuana were not successful, the legalization battle continued to gain momentum. In response to a question from a medical marijuana user, Ron Paul, a Texas Congressman and two-time presidential candidate, stated that he would "never use the federal government to enforce the law against anybody using marijuana."

On November 6, 2012, Colorado and Washington became the first states to legalize the sale and possession of marijuana for recreational use. Both states allowed possession of up to an ounce for adults ages 21 and older, and regulated marijuana similar to alcohol. Driving under the influence of drugs or "DUID" provisions were similar to those for drunk driving. Both states established guidelines for commercial cultivation and sales and subjected their state's new industry to stringent regulation and special taxes. Colorado's constitutional amendment also allowed the personal cultivation of up to six plants.

In August 2013, the cable channel CNN aired the first of three *Weed* documentaries in which Dr. Sanjay Gupta extolled the medical benefits of marijuana. The first *Weed* documentary featured the story of six-year-old Charlotte Figi, who suffered from Dravet Syndrome and benefited from medical marijuana. CNN's airing of the first *Weed* documentary was seen as instrumental in changing the hearts and minds of many Americans who were previously opposed to marijuana for medical purposes.

The American public's growing acceptance of marijuana influenced many elected officials to act. In 2013, Portland, Maine legalized the possession of up to 2.5 ounces of marijuana for recreational use, making it the first city on the East Coast to do so. Portland's citizens passed the law with 67 percent of the vote. Voters in other towns and cities took similar action.

In response to the actions by voters in Colorado and Washington, in 2013 the U.S. Department of Justice stated:

> ... based on assurances that those states will impose an appropriately strict regulatory system, the Department has informed the governors of both states that it is deferring its right to challenge their legalization laws at this time.[67]

With the tacit green light from the Department of Justice, Colorado Governor John Hickenlooper signed two bills enacting the provisions of the amendment to Colorado's constitution into law. Hickenlooper's actions made Colorado the world's first legal recreational marijuana market for adults. Hickenlooper explained to the media:

Certainly, this industry will create jobs. Whether it's good for the brand of our state is still up in the air. But the voters passed Amendment 64 by a clear majority. That's why we're going to implement it as effectively as we possibly can.

This movement to legalize marijuana was reflected in a Pew Research Center poll released in early 2013. It indicated that 52 percent of Americans supported legalizing marijuana, an upward spike of 11 percent since their previous poll in 2010. By February 2014, the percentage of respondents supporting legalization had increased to 54 percent.

Surrounded by great fanfare, America's first legal marijuana stores officially opened in Colorado at the stroke of midnight, January 1, 2014. As the State prepared for an influx of tourists, extra police officers were posted throughout Denver and other towns and cities, including the ski resort of Breckenridge, where lines began forming early on New Year's Eve.

While many fears had been raised, they were unfounded and Colorado's recreational marijuana launch went off without any significant issues.

Since 2014, various ballot initiatives to legalize recreational marijuana in other states were attempted. Some were successful, such as Oregon's Measure 80 and Alaska's Measure 2, while others, like California's Proposition 19, were not.

Many activists and supporters of marijuana legalization viewed the passage of state ballot initiatives as significant milestones and the first dominos to fall. However, to this day it remains unclear as to how the conflicts of the states' legalization with the illegality under federal law will be resolved.

Marijuana Policy Project Political Director, David Boyer, expressed the views of many when he said:

I think there's national implications, keeping the momentum that Washington and Colorado started last November in ending marijuana prohibition. There are hopes that the vote will be a push to legalize it statewide within the next few years.

In February 2014, President Obama signed the Agricultural Act of 2014 into law. It allowed the legal cultivation of industrial hemp for the first time in 59 years. While only allowing the growing of hemp for research and development purposes, it was seen as a significant change in policy. Hemp advocates were hopeful that Obama's action would lead to farmers being able to commercially growing hemp for its fiber and seeds, as well as developing hemp cultivars with high levels of CBD and low levels of THC for medicinal purposes.

Later in 2014, the *New York Times,*in an editorial series entitled *High Time an Editorial Series on Marijuana Legalization,* joined the bandwagon calling for the legalization of marijuana. The first editorial concluded with the statement:

We recognize that this Congress is as unlikely to take action on marijuana as it has been on other big issues. But it is long past time to repeal this version of Prohibition.

Numerous other factors contributed to the continuing change in attitudes, legislation and regulation at the local level. These included increased support from the healthcare community and the growing awareness by state and local governments that marijuana was a new potential source of tax revenue.

The federal spending bill that was signed into law in December 2014 included a provision blocking the Justice Department from spending any money to enforce the Federal ban on growing or selling marijuana in the 23 states that had legalized it for medical use. This was seen as a huge shift by Congress, which had historically sided with federal prosecutors and the DEA in their battles with states over the liberalization of drug laws.

In 2015, the federal government slightly lightened up its bureaucratic obstacles to medical marijuana research by eliminating the Public Health Service review process for non-federally funded research. Previously what had been required to research the medical benefits of marijuana hadn't been required for any other drugs, including heroin and cocaine.

As of November 2015, 28 American states had enacted laws decriminalizing the medical use of marijuana, eliminated jail time for possession of small amounts of marijuana, or legalized the possession, distribution, and sale of marijuana outright.

Legalization of Marijuana in U.S. Territories

In 2014, Guam became the first U.S. territory to legalize marijuana for medical use, followed by Puerto Rico in 2015. In late 2014, the U.S. Virgin Islands decriminalized the possession of less than an ounce of marijuana.

Legalization of Marijuana on Native American Lands

In December 2014, the U.S. Justice Department allowed recognized Native American tribes to regulate the growing and selling of marijuana on tribal lands. The government indicated that it would not intervene if the tribes regulated and maintained control over the production and sale of marijuana.

Some native American tribes were enthusiastic regarding the possibility of a new industry. Others were opposed, seeing the potential for substance abuse as similar to problems that existed on tribal lands with alcohol.

The Yakama Nation and the Oglala Sioux Tribal Council rejected allowing marijuana on their tribal lands.[68] In 2015, the Flandreau Santee Sioux Tribe of South Dakota voted to legalize recreational marijuana on its tribal lands.

PART THREE: Breeding and Growing Marijuana

Chapter 14: Breeding Marijuana for Desired Characteristics

"Why use up the forests which were centuries in the making and the mines, which required ages to lay down, if we can get the equivalent of forest and mineral products in the annual growth of hemp fields.

Henry Ford

Just as cannabis had a significant impact on the evolution of mankind, mankind has had a significant impact on the evolution of cannabis, a relationship that continues today.

Tall, sturdy cannabis plants were grown by early civilizations to produce a variety of foods, oils, and textiles, including rope and fabric. As these plants were bred with other plants with similar characteristics, strains of cannabis evolved that are described today as hemp.

Other cannabis varieties were valued for their psychoactive and healing properties and were bred for medical, religious and spiritual purposes. This led to unique varieties of cannabis that we refer to as marijuana.

The prevalent scientific consensus is that the cannabis gene pool separated early. Some plants were bred and grown for fiber and seeds, and other plants were bred and grown for medicine or psychoactive effects. This led to two distinct types of cannabis plants, the two subspecies, Cannabis indica and Cannabis sativa.

There is a distinct difference between growing and breeding marijuana. Growing is the simple cultivation of plants. Breeding is the science of manipulating the propagation of plants to emphasize or eliminate specific characteristics. In traditional agriculture, the most common desired traits are better nutritional value, improved flavor, increased crop yield, and resistance to disease. For marijuana, desired traits include resin content, the flower to leaf ratio, vigor, potency, taste, aroma, maturation cycle and resistance to mold and mites.

The creation of a new marijuana seed line or strain is part art and part science. When plants of one strain are crossed with another strain, the resulting generation (F1) is referred to as a hybrid. The offspring will not be identical to either parent and instead will have characteristics of both parents. It often takes several generations before desired characteristics appear with regularity.

Breeding can be achieved through a variety of techniques ranging from simply placing plants with the desired characteristics in the same vicinity for natural pollination, to complex molecular engineering.

Breeding of Marijuana in the 21st Century

Since the 1970s, most of the marijuana grown in the U.S was indoors due to a fear of legal prosecution. Indoor growing and the ability of a breeder or grower to manipulate the growing environment facilitated and accelerated the breeding of plants with desired characteristics.

Typically, the most desired marijuana characteristic was a high level of THC. This was driven by the desire of recreational marijuana users for a higher content of the psychoactive cannabinoid. It is safe to say that today's marijuana is not your father's marijuana.

Marijuana plants, like most other living things, inherit their genetic characteristics from their parents. The natural laws of heredity enable a breeder to forecast the number of offspring that should inherit a specific trait. A true, or pure breed is critical in the breeding process to ensure that the genetic makeup of the offspring is relatively uniform and common traits are established.

If the parent plants are not a pure breed, the traits of the future generations of the hybrids are impossible to predict. Furthermore, somewhere between the fourth and sixth generation of inbreeding, negative characteristics such as low potency tend to become dominate.

Inbreeding

Inbreeding is the creation of offspring by breeding plants that are genetically closely related. The chosen females are bred back or "back-crossed" with males of the same strain. This establishes a true breed or strain; plants with the same growth characteristics.

Inbreeding does not add or subtract traits from a breeding line, but it does accelerate the appearance of recessive traits, enabling the breeder to determine if they are positive or negative.

Once the ancestry and growth characteristics become known, a plant can be used to breed hybrid plants. While inbreeding is effective for establishing a pure breed, it is not a desirable technique to use once the new strain has been established.

Outbreeding

Outbreeding is the crossing of two plants with different genetic backgrounds. An F1 hybrid is the first generation from crossing two breeding plants, and these are the most desired plants. They often grow 25 percent more quickly and become larger than other crosses. This is known as hybrid vigor, which subsequent generations of the plant lack.

The offspring of F1 plants are referred to as F2, and the offspring of F2 are referred to as F3, and this numbering system continues for future generations.

A stable growing environment allows plants to develop their genetic traits without interference. If a plant is stressed or its environment is changed, genetic characteristics may be affected. Examples of environmental stress include plants being subjected to extreme temperatures, insufficient water, or a change in the photoperiod.

The result of stressed plants can be abnormal flowers or reversal of sex. This can include some male flowers on a plant that is predominately female. These plants are not natural hermaphrodites, but instead stressed plants with intersex tendencies that manifest as hermaphrodite plants. The alteration of a plant's sex through environmental stress can affect future generations and can cause the genetic deviation to be passed on to subsequent generations.

Backcrossing

Backcrossing, or breeding plants with their offspring, is a technique that breeders use to increase the incidence of a certain trait within a strain.

The first step is finding or developing a marijuana strain that has desired characteristics. These could include a greater production of resin or a specific level of CBD or THC. The objective is then to create a seed line that will consistently replicate that desired characteristics or traits of the selected plant. This is achieved through a combination of cloning and backcrossing, or "cubing."

The next step of the process is to clone and propagate the "mother" of the selected plant. This is done by taking a cutting from the mother plant. The clone serves as a surrogate, ensuring a consistent genetic base for all future generations throughout the breeding process.

Next, a flowering clone is crossed with pollen from males related to the selected plant, usually "brother" plants whose genetic makeup also includes 50 percent of the mother's phenotype.[1] This results is an F1 generation of seeds with 75 percent of the desired genetics; 50 percent from the cloned mother, and 25 percent from the brother.

The male offspring of the F1 seeds, as well as those of subsequent generations, are then crossed with the clones of the original mother female, each time increasing the percentage of the desired genetic makeup. The second backcross is called squaring, and the resulting F2 seeds carry 87.5% of the desired genetics. If done correctly, the third backcrossing, or cubing, will generate seeds comprising nearly 94 percent of the selected female's genetics, which is generally accepted as a pure breed.

---

[1] A phenotype is the composite of a plant's observable characteristics or traits

MARIJUANA: The World's Most Misunderstood Plant

Chapter 15: Cultivating Marijuana

"That is not a drug, it's a leaf."

Arnold Schwarzenegger

One of cannabis' nicknames, "weed" has led many to assume that growing good marijuana is simple. This is a fallacy. The cultivation of healthy marijuana requires specific conditions for the plant to thrive. Although every marijuana grower has his or her preferred methods, whether from seed, clone or tissue culture, the growing of the plant is essentially the same.

Cultivation is also influenced by the growing environment, such as whether the grow will occur indoors, outdoors or in greenhouses, each of which has its advantages and disadvantages.

Growing Marijuana from Seeds

Growing marijuana from seeds is the most stable method and is how the plant propagates in nature. There are many advantages to growing marijuana from seed, most notably, it's easy, especially for small-scale growing. Assuming the genetics of the seeds are known, the plants will generally be consistent, with predictable results.

Marijuana grown from seeds tend to have a hearty root structure, including a tap root. The tap root is the central part of a plant's entire root system, extending deep into the surrounding soil, enabling the plant to easily absorb nutrients from the ground, or growing medium.

Another advantage of growing from seeds is the ability to identify feminized seeds. Since only female plants produce buds with trichomes containing cannabinoids, growing female plants is generally the objective of most growers. The ability to plant only feminized seeds enables growers to have the desired outcome.

Growing Marijuana from Clones

A clone is a plant grown from a cutting of a mature marijuana plant. The primary advantage of growing from clones is the knowledge of the offspring's genetics. Since clones are cut from another plant, they start as a genetic copy of the source plant. Another big advantage is the speed at which plants can be harvested, as clones mature much faster than plants grown from seeds.

It may sound simple to grow a plant from a cutting, but it can be a struggle to keep young clones healthy. Transplant failure is common.

Critical to successful growing from clones is starting with a strong plant. Because a clone is an exact genetic copy of the mother plant, if the mother plant had health issues, the clone will also have those issues. If the cutting is from a plant that is old, it may yield clones with fewer buds than a plant grown from seed.

A freshly cut clone needs attention when it is first replanted since there is an initial period of transplant shock. The period of transplant shock increases the plants' susceptibility to disease, including fungus. Since clones start from a cutting rather than from seed, they are incapable of growing a tap root. Because of the lack of a tap root, clones never are as strong and healthy as plants grown from seeds.

A logical conclusion is that adult cannabis plants grown from clones should be genetically identical to the mother plant. But, this is not always the case. Characteristics and traits can vary, and these variations can be passed on to the next generation, even though they are derived from genetically identical cells. This "genetic drift" is caused by DNA mutations in the clone that were not present in the genome of the mother plant.

Many experienced growers prefer growing from seeds with the objective of growing higher quality plants. Other growers have raised generation after generation of plants from clones and believe it is the optimal method.

Tissue Culture Marijuana Propagation

Tissue culture propagation, which is also referred to as micropropagation or in-vitro propagation, is having a tremendous impact on the marijuana industry. The process involves growing new plants from parts of another plant, such as the shoot tip, node or leaves.

In the past, tissue culture propagation was conducted in a laboratory environment, requiring expensive equipment. However, the technology has evolved and costs have significantly decreased making it accessible to a greater number of growers. Today, using biocides and a sterile culture box, growers with small-scale operations can produce hundreds of small plantlets, which can then be grown indoors, outdoors or in a greenhouse.

Assuming a grower has the facilities and know-how for tissue culture propagation, they can grow plants that require less light, water, nutrients and space. The process also enables growers to multiply the plant's genetic material without changing the genetics.

Tissue culture propagation enables thousands of plants to be cultured at one time, the plants retain their genetic structure, and the resistance to disease typically increases.

Chapter 16: Growing to Maximize the Plant's Quality

Many factors contribute to the optimal cultivation of healthy marijuana plants. Nutrients, temperature, light, and water, are all important. Whether the objective is growing a hemp plant high in fiber, or a trichome-rich marijuana plant with a specific cannabinoid profile, cultivating to maximize the desired qualities is a delicate balancing act.

Nutrients

As with all plants, marijuana obtains nutrients from its environment. Whether it's grown in soil, hydroponically, or aeroponically, growing high-quality plants requires nutrients, which are typically provided with fertilizers and supplements.

The optimal combination of nutrients is a function of the environment in which the plant is grown and the desired characteristics. Usually, the primary nutrients consist of a combination of nitrogen, phosphorus, and potassium. Secondary nutrients, which include sulfur, magnesium and calcium are also often added.

Once the formula of the nutrients is decided, it is necessary to determine the quantity and frequency of application. Too much fertilizer can burn a plant, too little results in the depletion of the soil's nutrients.

The nutritional requirements are also a function of the particular strain and the stage of the plant's growth. For example, during the vegetative stage, marijuana plants require more nitrogen than phosphorus and potassium. During the flowering phase, phosphorus is typically more important than nitrogen or potassium.

There are general guidelines for the appropriate nutrients for growing marijuana, but they vary widely depending on the growing environment and the particular strain. This results in the optimal nutrient formula often being determined by trial and error.

Temperature

Temperature is the most consistent factor in growing marijuana. The optimal temperature range is between 75° to 86° Fahrenheit. While some strains can withstand a light frost, generally temperatures above 88° and below 60° negatively impact the plants' overall growth and decrease the potency of the plant's cannabinoids.

Light

Periods of light and darkness are necessary for healthy flowers to form. For most strains, flowering is induced by changing the plant's light schedule, which triggers a hormonal reaction within the plant. This occurs when the duration of darkness is increased.

Indica and sativa lack a defined flowering stage and have different light cycles. Indica require as little as eight hours of darkness to begin flowering while some sativa strains require up to thirteen hours. Ruderalis do not have a defined flowering stage and are an auto-flowering Cannabis subspecies.

For growers using artificial light, the typical procedure is to use a regime of 16 to 20 hours of light and 4 to 8 hours of darkness from germination through flowering. At this stage, the cannabis plant can also withstand a full 24 hours of daily light without hampering its growth.

The total number of hours for the "dark period" often leads to contentious discussions between marijuana growers. Most growers have a strong opinion. Research has indicated that when subjected to constant light without a dark period, marijuana will begin to show signs of decreased photosynthetic response, a general lack of good health and an overall decrease in vascular development.

Marijuana grown outdoors naturally flower in response to the change of the length of days as fall approaches. Growers have found ways to manipulate the outdoor growing environment with artificial lighting and shade canopies.

Water

Water is critical element for growing healthy marijuana, but as with the other factors, the optimal quantity and frequency of watering varies by strain and growing environment. Factors that influence the required amount and frequency of watering include the temperature, light conditions, the soil or growing medium's ability to retain water, and the specific plant's age, size, and stage of growth. Too little water causes plants to wilt. Too much water may drown the plant's cells. At either extreme of watering, the plants may die.

The source of water also must be considered. Spring and well water are preferred sources. Household tap water usually contains additives that can negatively impact a plant's growth. These additives can be removed with reverse osmosis filtration, a process that can be expensive. Generally, filtered tap water produces poorer quality plants than plants grown with spring or well water.

Chapter 17: The Marijuana Plant's Growth Cycle

To truly understand the growth cycle of a marijuana plant, it is necessary to have an appreciation of the entire cultivation process. Growing cycles of marijuana plants are similar to those of other species of flowering plants. The main phases of a marijuana plant's growth are germination, seedling, vegetative, pre-flowering, flowering and harvest.

The Germination Phase

Germination is the process of preparing seeds for cultivation. This is done by initiating the seed's metabolic processes and activating the hormones that trigger the expansion of the embryo within the seed. Most seeds require a sufficient quantity of water to moisten the seeds but not enough to soak them. This leads to the swelling and the breaking of the seed coat. For marijuana seeds, this occurs anywhere between twelve hours and eight days.

Germination is also affected by temperature, light and moisture. It can be initiated by soaking the seeds in a cup of warm water, between wet paper towels, in peat pellets or directly in the soil.

Once the seed coat cracks open, an embryonic root emerges and begins growing in the direction of gravitational pull.

Peat pellets are beneficial as a germinating medium since the entire pellets with the seedlings can be planted directly into the soil or growing medium with minimal shock to the plant.

The Seedling Phase

The seedling phase is the most vulnerable time of a marijuana plant's life. It typically lasts from one to four weeks. Seedlings require moderate humidity levels, medium to high light intensity and adequate, but not excessive moisture.

When the seedling emerges from the seed coat and starts growing roots, its food reserves become exhausted. It then relies on external sources of water and nutrients.

The Vegetative Phase

Once the young plant has seven sets of leaves and the eighth is just visible in the center of the growth tip, the plant has entered its vegetative, or veg phase. When marijuana is grown indoors, the vegetative phase usually ranges from one to two months.

The vegetative phase is the plant's formative growing stage. During this phase, the plant directs all of its resources to the growth of roots, stems and leaves, which are critical for the strong development of flowers.

Some auto-flowering hybrid strains, typically developed from ruderalis strains, omit the vegetative phase and proceed directly from the seedling to a pre-flowering phase.

Plants in the vegetative phase require a significant amount of light, although amounts vary based on the plant's genetics.

During the vegetative phase, indoor growers typically induce an 18 to 24-hour photoperiod, since marijuana plants tend to grow more quickly if they receive more light.

During the vegetative phase, many growers will use fertilizers high in nitrogen and potassium, and micro-nutrients, slowly increasing the strength of the fertilizer as the plant continues to grow.

Training

As plants mature, growers frequently manipulate the growth pattern, a process called training. The objective is to encourage a shorter and denser canopy growth. There are several training methods, some are minimal and some severe. Training techniques can be used individually, but frequently two or more are used together.

One variation of training is trimming. It consists of pruning certain parts of the plant so its resources are devoted to the development and growth of other areas. For example, smaller growth shoots and suckers near the bottom of the plant are often removed as they typically receive little light and, therefore, produce poor quality buds.

Another trimming technique is topping, which consists of the removal of the top of a plant's dominant central stem. Topping usually results in rapid growth of all of the branches below the cut, while the top of the plant is healing.

Pinching, or super-cropping, is a training technique performed by firmly pinching the dominant central stem. This damages the plant's vascular system and structural cells of the stem without totally breaking them. Similar to topping, this causes the lower branches to grow more rapidly while the pinched tissue heals.

Low-stress training is a less aggressive form of super cropping. It consists of bending the plant's branches to form the plant into the desired shape. This training technique is useful for indoor growers who use artificial light. The intensity of the light is greatly reduced for the parts of the plant that are farther from the light source. Low-stress training is used to ensure that all the growth tips are at the same approximate distance from the light source.

The Pre-Flowering or Stretch Phase

The pre-flowering, or stretch phase can range anywhere from one day to two weeks. For indoor growing, this phase typically starts ten to fourteen days after the plant's light cycle is switched to twelve hours of darkness and twelve hours of light.

During the pre-flowering phase, the plant's development increases dramatically, and the plant can more than double in size. It will form branches and nodes that will eventually develop flowers.

It is the pre-flowering phase when the plant begins to develop identifiable sex characteristics. The size of the plant is a good indicator of the plant's sex. Female plants tend to be shorter and have more branches than males, which tend to be taller with fewer leaves. Most growers are only interested in growing female plants since it is unpollinated female plants that develop the buds that contain cannabinoids. It is important that careful attention is paid to the plants during this stage and that male plants are immediately removed when their sex becomes known to prevent fertilization of the female plants.

When the objective of growing is the production of seeds, and not growing for bud-containing cannabinoids, separating male and female plants provides control over which male plants fertilize the female plants. Frequently, growers capture the pollen produced by the male plants and store it until needed.

The Flowering Phase

The flowering phase is a critical growth phase since the plant's flowers contain the greatest quantity of trichomes, and, therefore, the greatest quantity of cannabinoids.

Most marijuana plants begin to flower under diminishing periods of light, whether grown indoors or outdoors. Marijuana grown outdoors begins flowering in response to the plant's natural light cycle, with up to 18 hours of light per day in the summer, and less than 12 hours per day in the fall and winter.

Flowering is induced by subjecting plants to at least 10 hours of darkness per day. There is often a debate among growers as to the optimal period of required darkness. More hours of daily darkness tend to accelerate the flowering period, but also result in a decreased number of flowers and buds. Conversely, fewer hours of darkness results in a longer overall flowering period, resulting in an increased quantity of flowers and buds.

Marijuana flowers are referred to as bract/bracteole and usually begin to develop one to two weeks after the reduction of the duration of the photoperiod. During the first weeks of flowering, marijuana plants typically double, and some may triple in size. The development of bract and bracteole ends around five weeks after the beginning of the flowering phase.

The flowering hormone is present during all phases of a plant's growth but is inhibited by exposure to light. Pure indica strains typically flower for 45 to 60 days, and sativa strains will usually require between 60 and 90 days to finish blooming. The duration of the flowering phase of hybrid strains typically ranges between those of indica and sativa strains.

MARIJUANA: The World's Most Misunderstood Plant

As the flowering phase nears its end, unpollinated female plants begin producing buds covered with sticky resinous trichomes. This is a natural biological function and is the last attempt by the plant for pollination by windborne pollen.

The flowering period is followed by a period of bract/bracteole "swelling" during which the buds increase substantially in weight and size.

Harvesting

The final stage in a marijuana plant's life cycle is the harvest. Once the plant has flowered, the time for harvesting must be determined. If plants are harvested too early, the yield of cannabinoids will not be maximized. If harvesting occurs too late, the plant's trichomes will start to degrade resulting in a reduced quantity of cannabinoids.

There are several ways to determine when marijuana plants are ready to be harvested. The simplest way is to look at the buds. At the onset of flowering, the pistils are white and stringy. While the change in color varies with the strain, toward the end of the flowering period the pistils will change color from white to orange and then again to a dark red or brown.

Once harvested, the plants are dried in preparation for further processing, for either the production of buds and plant material for smoking or vaping, or for extraction.

PART FOUR – Consuming Marijuana

Chapter 18: Marijuana as a Psychoactive Substance

"When you smoke the herb, it reveals you to yourself"

Bob Marley

Recreational users consume marijuana for both the plant's psychoactive and physiological effects. These include relaxation or euphoria or a state of intense excitement.[1] These effects are a biological response to the interaction of cannabinoids and terpenes with the user's endocannabinoid system. Since each individual is affected differently and has varying experiences, one person may feel relief from stress, another may feel over-stimulated and stressed while yet others may feel energized and focused.

The Impact of Different Strains

Just as every individual has a unique biological makeup, so does every marijuana plant. Each plant's genetic makeup is affected by its environment. Some of these factors include the

---

[1] For purposes of this book, all non-medical uses are considered recreational, and therefore include spiritual and religious uses.

plant's strain, growing environment, access to nutrients, and harvest cycle, some of which are more predictable than others.

Sativa strains typically affect one's feelings and thoughts. Therefore, many prefer it for daytime use. Sativa are generally beneficial in stimulating creativity. For others, sativa reduce depression and elevate one's mood. Typically, one's appetite is increased, commonly referred to as the "munchies." Adverse effects also may result. For instance, some users find that sativa strains increase their anxiety and create feelings of paranoia.

The primary effects of indica are on the body. Indicas tend to produce sedated or calming feelings, making the strain beneficial for relaxation and for reducing stress. Indica can be helpful as a sleep aid and can reduce anxiety. Similar to the effect of sativa, indica may increase one's appetite. Some users find that indica strains cause tiredness or "fuzzy thinking," with many users preferring indicas for nighttime use.

It's difficult to generalize regarding the effects of hybrid strains. The primary effects of hybrids are generally tied to the dominant strain. If the dominant strain is a sativa strain, then the effects are generally as one would expect from sativa. Likewise, hybrids with a dominant indica strain, produce results one would expect from indica strains.

Other Considerations

Obviously the amount ingested, the strain of plant and method of ingestion are important, however, other factors that affect an indivdual's response to marijuana are the individual's biochemistry and history of marijuana use, as well as the person's mindset or mood at the time of consumption. Other factors include the particular strain, the amount ingested, and the method of ingestion.

Chapter 19: Smoking Marijuana

"Of course I know how to roll a joint."

Martha Stewart

Until recently, the mention of marijuana brought to mind the image of hippies toking on a joint. Despite many safer alternatives, smoking marijuana is still part of American culture and a social activity. For many, passing a joint among friends is a perfect way to spend an evening.

Although it is counter-intuitive, smoking marijuana is also the primary way most patients ingest the plant for medicinal purposes. In part, this is because it is the only approved method of access for patients who want to use marijuana-based medicine in many jurisdictions. Until recently, this was the case in Israel and Canada, where their national healthcare systems only allowed patients to obtain marijuana in a form for smoking. Extracts, concentrates, and edible products were not allowed.

The limited access to methods of ingestion other than smoking is a growing concern for many patients and healthcare professionals. The smoke generated by burning marijuana contains many of the same carcinogenic compounds that are contained in tobacco smoke, including the hydrocarbons and tar that have been identified as key factors in increasing the risk of lung cancer. Tar is toxic and damages the smoker's lungs over time through various biochemical processes. Tar can also damage the mouth by damaging gums, rotting and blackening teeth, and desensitizing taste buds.

Part of the challenge in determining the impact of smoking marijuana on the human body is that many regular marijuana smokers are also cigarette smokers. There is a general consensus that marijuana smoke irritates the lungs and increases the exposure to carcinogens and other toxins. Frequent smoking of marijuana is also believed to contribute to "smokers cough," more frequent chest illnesses, and a greater risk of lung infections.

There is, however, no direct evidence linking the smoking of marijuana to any health risks, including lung cancer. Many researchers acknowledge that it took decades to establish a similar link between tobacco, lung cancer, and other adverse health effects, so there are health concerns.

Chapter 20: Marijuana Concentrates and Extracts

"If one seeks relief from unbearable pressure, one is to eat hashish."

Friedrich Nietzsche

The terms concentrates and extracts are often used interchangeably. They are a potent consolidation of cannabinoids extracted from the plant material. Concentrates and extracts, and the products manufactured from them, including edibles, provide the ability to consume cannabis without having to smoke the plant material.

Concentrates are the fastest growing segment of the legal cannabis industry. The growing popularity of concentrates will likely continue as an increasing number of recreational and medical consumers become aware of the advantages.

Concentrates are manufactured by a variety of processes, called extraction. These extraction processes all have the same objectives, the separation of the cannabinoids from the dried cannabis flowers, or "buds" and the plant's leaves, stalks, and branches, or "trim." Trim also contains cannabinoids, but the content is significantly less than that contained in the buds.

Regardless of the extraction method used, the end-product is referred to as a concentrate or extract.

The potency of concentrates provides recreational users with a quicker and more intense psychoactive experience. The THC content of many concentrates can be as high as 80 percent, compared to around 30 percent, for some higher THC buds for smoking.

Medical users find concentrates attractive because they can ingest stronger doses without having to smoke large quantities of the marijuana plant material. Some methods of ingesting concentrates also provide more immediate relief.

Commercial extractors have recognized the flexibility concentrates provide for the development of numerous marijuana-based products. Concentrates provide manufacturers with the ability to make end-products derived from marijuana plants that have high levels of THC, high-levels of CBD, combinations of both, and some of the other cannabinoids.

Concentrates are also used in the manufacture of topical ointments and lotions, capsules and liquid tinctures. Concentrates have made it possible for manufacturers to offer extensive products lines, including edibles and "ready-to-drink" products such as teas and nutritional drinks.

As more states legalize marijuana, it is increasingly viewed as something of a commodity and the market is becoming extremely competitive. As these trends continue, concentrates provide commercial growers and extractors with the ability to sell higher-margin products, that can be more profitable than selling buds for smoking.

Cannabinoid Extraction Methods

There are a variety of ways to produce concentrates. The objective of all the methods is to separate, or "extract" the cannabinoids from the plant material. Individuals who produce

119

high-quality extracts are often referred to as "extract artists," with each having their preferred extraction method.

Since cannabinoids are not water soluble, extractors separate the cannabinoids from the plant material by dissolving them in a solvent.

Until very recently, the most popular solvent used for extraction was butane. This is largely attributed to the illegality of marijuana, as extraction was also a clandestine and illegal activity. Since butane has several common household uses, it was easy to procure without suspicion. A disadvantage of butane is its flammability, thus butane extraction is a potentially dangerous activity, particularly for novices.

Scientific advances led to the development of new extraction techniques that incorporate water, ice, CO_2, butane, hexane, isopropyl alcohol, and ethanol. Each have their advantages and disadvantages, but provide alternatives to butane extraction.

The Traditional Method of Producing Hashish

> *"When you return to this mundane sphere from your visionary world, you would seem to leave a Neapolitan spring for a Lapland winter – to quit paradise for earth–heaven for hell! Taste the hashish, guest of mine – taste the hashish!"*

Alexander Dumas

A good starting point to gain a basic understanding of extraction is to examine the centuries-old techniques developed in the Hindu Kush tribal regions of Pakistan and Afghanistan. These methods produced hashish, or as it's more commonly known, hash.

Hashish is believed to have originated on the hands and tools of farmers as they separated mature marijuana flowers from the rest of the plant. As they harvested the plants, trichome resin would stick to their hands and leave residue on the sieves that were being used to separate the buds. Rubbing their hands together caused the resin to form little balls, with a consistency similar to that of rubber cement. The same thing occurred with the residue on the sieves. When these little clusters were kneaded together, they formed a paste, often referred to as "finger hash."

This process was eventually scaled up to maximize the yield of hashish from each harvest.

The Dry Sift Extraction of Producing Hashish

The dry sift process starts by drying the harvested cannabis plants, first in the field, and then indoors. The dried material is then threshed and sieved to separate the buds and trichomes from the rest of the plant. The residue is referred to by different names in different locales, but the most common is "garda." Garda consists of dried resin, but it also contains other plant material.

The garda is hit against a drum or barrel to separate the dried buds, leaves, and seeds from the twigs and branches which are usually later used as fuel for cooking. The residual powder is then collected and sieved again through a cloth covered wooden frame, called a cot. This sieving process is usually repeated three times, which improves the purity of the resin.

The sieved material is put into a cloth bag, which is shaken vigorously to filter out as much dust as possible. The remaining powder is put into smaller pouches and beaten by hand to further remove remaining dust. What remains at this stage is mostly resin. Based on the quantity and quality of the resin, it is categorized as first garda, second garda or third garda. The first garda has the highest amount of resin, and, therefore, brings the highest price. Most farmers sell the garda to traders for the final processing to turn it into hashish, although some farmers process it into hashish themselves.

The final process of making hashish consists of pressing small amounts of the garda powder between one's palms, letting the heat from the hands turn the resin into a paste. If quality garda has been produced, the product is sticky and compresses into somewhat of a glob.

Lastly, the garda is heated over a low flame. This is sometimes referred to as cooking. This step converts the garda material to hashish and it's then described as cooked. Both the rubbing between one's palms and the cooking may be repeated several times.

Modern Dry Sieve Extraction

Over the past few decades, improvements have been made to the dry sift method. Silk screens have replaced cloth sieves, machines are now frequently used to agitate and press the garda, and other variations have developed in various Hindu Kush regions. The result is a very traditional type of concentrate that is typically ingested by smoking, but it can also be used in the production of edibles, vaporized or dabbed.

Similar to wine aficionados, there are also concentrate connoisseurs. Because the dry sieve method employs a meticulous process that removes the trichomes from the cannabis plant without the use of chemicals, many concentrate connoisseurs consider it the optimal extraction method.

One downside of this dry sieve method of extraction is the low yield of concentrates it produces, compared to most other extraction methods.

Water Extraction

Water extraction evolved from the traditional manufacture of hashish. The plant material, which may itself be frozen, is mixed with cold water and ice to freeze the trichomes. The trichomes become brittle and break away from the other plant material. The solution that results is then filtered through a series of micron-sized screens to remove the unwanted materials.

Once extracted, the concentrate is thoroughly dried. This is a critical step to avoid the development of mold.

Many consider water extraction the purest method since the trichomes aren't dissolved by the water. Once the trichomes are removed from the plant they are easily separated from the solution. This is unlike solvent-based methods where the trichomes are actually dissolved and then the solvent is removed through another chemical process.

Concentrates produced using water extraction are called water hash, bubble hash, iceolate, solvent-less, and ice-wax. These extracts often test between 50 percent and 80 percent THC.

Light Hydrocarbon Extraction

The most common extraction methods that use hydrocarbons as solvents require propane and butane. These methods are often preferred by home extractors. The attraction of hydrocarbon extraction is its simplicity and low cost.

A downside to this method is the risk of combustion. Butane and propane both extract cannabinoids effectively, but when things go badly, explosions occur.

The negative view of butane extraction was furthered by numerous television, newspaper and online reports of college dorm rooms and apartments exploding in the midst of extractions. This resulted in some fire and building codes banning the process for commercial purposes and many municipalities banning its residential use.

These explosions have hindered the marijuana legalization movement and frequently resulted in marijuana being talked about in the same terms as the manufacture of methamphetamines.

Another side effect of butane or propane extraction is that the concentrate produced can contain contaminants. While butane and propane are considered non-toxic and frequently used in the food and cosmetic industries, the equipment used in the extraction process may add contaminants which can be a health hazard.

Hexane Extraction

Hexane can be used as a solvent for extraction, but it is not as popular as butane or propane. This is because hexane is both extremely flammable and toxic.

The normal process for hexane extraction begins by mixing hexane and plant material in a container and shaking it vigorously. The lid is then loosened to release the pressure. It is then sealed again and set aside. This process is repeated periodically for up to about twelve hours. The extract is then forced through a strainer to force as much hexane out as possible. The resulting material is then filtered through a sieve.

The next step is to purge the hexane from the mixture. This can be done using vacuum equipment or by washing the extract with ethanol. The extract dissolves in the ethanol, which is then burned off. Because the boiling point of ethanol is higher than that of hexane, the boiling eliminates the hexane.

The final step consists of freezing the remaining ethanol-based product for two to three days. The waxes coagulate, are filtered out, and the ethanol evaporates.

CO$_2$ Extraction

CO$_2$ extraction is one of the least toxic-forms of extraction. Estimates indicate that more than 90 percent of commercial extraction is done using CO$_2$. However, CO$_2$ extraction equipment is expensive and can range upwards of $100,000, which is prohibitively expensive for at-home extractors.

The equipment compresses CO2 at such a high pressure that it becomes a "supercritical fluid" which is then employed as a solvent to strip the essential oils from the cannabis plant. CO2 is not flammable and the process uses no chemical solvents.

Concentrates produced by CO2 extractions are growing in popularity. They are increasingly used in the production of edibles, tinctures, oils and capsules as well as the production of a variety of recreational concentrates.

CO2 extraction equipment is manufactured by numerous companies. Most of the equipment is similar, with a basic model processing around 20 liters of plant material over a 24-hour period. Large, commercial extraction facilities have been engineered and constructed to process 100 to 1000 pounds of plant material a day, but the costs of these large systems can easily reach millions of dollars.

Isopropyl Alcohol Extraction

Isopropyl alcohol can be used as a solvent to produce concentrates through the "quick wash" method.

Since isopropyl alcohol is water soluble, it easily dissolves the cannabinoids The remaining plant material floats to the top of the mixture, which is then sieved and dried.

Types of Marijuana Concentrates and Extracts

Concentrates are referred to by a variety of terms. The classification of concentrates is often dependent on the manufacturing method and the consistency of the final product.

Common names for concentrates include waxes, oils, budders and shatters, and, of course, hashish or hash.

Hashish

Hashish is the original concentrate and has been produced for centuries. Also referred to as hash, or just oil, it is produced by compressing the plant's resin. Hashish may be solid or resinous depending on the preparation. Pressed hashish is usually solid, whereas water-purified hashish has a granular feel.

Though not as potent as other concentrates, hashish remains a staple of the cannabis culture worldwide.

Budder and Wax

Budder is a concentrate that is essentially an opaque form of hash oil. Wax is the opaque, crumbly texture seen in hash that is generally produced by stirring the extracted concentrate over heat to add air.

The differences between budder and wax are subtle. Budder is softer and more pliable, with a consistency similar to that of butter at room temperature. Wax is generally crumblier.

Butane Hash or Honey Oil and BHO

Butane hash oil, which is also referred to as butane honey oil, BHO, or sometimes wax, is an extremely potent concentrate. BHO is known for its amber color.

As apparent from its name, butane hash oil is created using butane extraction. This results in a wax-like substance that either maintains its waxy and sticky consistency or hardens up resulting in a crumbly "honeycomb" type material or a glass-like "shatter."

BHO's content level of THC can often reach 80 percent, making the concentrate attractive for recreational users wanting a quick and intense high. It's also preferred by many patients suffering from chronic pain wanting quick relief.

Similar to other extraction methods that use butane, the downside of BHO is the potential of the end product having trace amounts of butane.

CO_2 Oil

CO2 oil is the byproduct of the CO2 extraction method. The end product is a gooey material that is typically cut with a thinning substance such as coconut oil or polypropylene glycol, resulting in an amber liquid.

Rick Simpson Oil or RSO

Originally developed in 2003 by Rick Simpson as a treatment for skin cancer, Rick Simpson Oil or RSO has evolved since then.[69]

Simpson manufactured his oil by soaking marijuana in pure naphtha, or isopropyl alcohol. The result was a tar-like substance which Simpson applied to his skin. He credited his concentrate with curing his skin cancer. Simpson then started using the oil as the basis for a tincture, which provided benefits for patients suffering from cancer and other medical conditions.

Simpson's product is also known as Phoenix Tears. It is available in a variety of formulations, some with high-levels of CBD and others with high-levels of THC. It is used for both recreational and medical purposes.

Tinctures

Tinctures are liquid concentrates which were historically produced through alcohol extraction methods. Today they are also produced using other methods, including CO2 extraction.

Tinctures are typically used as medicine or to provide other health benefits. They are ingested by squirting one or more drops under the tongue.

Before marijuana was essentially banned by the U.S. government in 1937, cannabis tinctures were a very common form of medicine, one in most doctor's bags.

Chapter 21: Marijuana Edibles

"I strained to remember where I was or even what I was wearing, touching my green corduroy jeans and staring at the exposed-brick wall. As my paranoia deepened, I became convinced that I had died and no one was telling me."

Maureen Dowd, New York Times Columnist

Edibles have gone way beyond the Alice B. Toklas brownies of the 1950s and 1960s. Because of advancements in marijuana breeding over the past sixty years, today's edibles are manufactured from marijuana strains that are many times more potent than at any other time in history.

Most, if not all of today's edibles are manufactured from concentrates or extracts and not marijuana buds. Improvements in marijuana extraction technology have accelerated the development and manufacture of new edible products.

The market for edibles has also been affected by the legalization of marijuana at the state-level. Legal markets have been a motivator for entrepreneurs seeing the manufacture of edibles as a profitable and legal enterprise. In some states, this has resulted in the availability of dozens, if not hundreds of edible products.

The market for edibles is seen as one of the fastest-growing segments of the U.S. marijuana industry. It's not uncommon for consumers to carry hard marijuana-based candies in their pocket, or lollipops in their purse.

As more states legalize marijuana for recreational or medical use, edible products are becoming available to a larger and larger audience. These new users include the elderly, many of whom are entirely new to marijuana and have no idea what to expect.

Recreational users are finding the surreptitious ability to get high provides an alternative way to use marijuana without the stigma of smoking a joint, pulling out a pocket-sized vaporizer, or a torch to dab. Brownies, cupcakes and candy bars are easy to eat at a concert or an NBA basketball game.

For patients who have never smoked, and don't want to smoke due to health concerns, edible products are an attractive alternative. For other medical marijuana users, including children, edibles are an easy way to ingest medicine. Edible users include sufferers of chronic pain, who can eat a few gummy bears or a cookie when they need relief. The downside for medical consumers is that edibles don't provide immediate relief. It typically takes at least thirty minutes for edibles to have an impact, and depending on the concentration of cannabinoids, the full effect might not be felt for a couple of hours.

In states where marijuana is legal, there are a variety of edibles available. These include chocolate chip and peanut butter cookies, fudge, caramels, chocolate truffles, chocolate bark toffees, lollipops, candy bars, candies, and cupcakes of various sizes. Edibles are also available as ready-to-drink products, including soft drinks, juices, lemonades, coffees and teas.

Many edible product lines include products that look remarkably like classic favorites, including Milky Way and Almond Joy candy bars, Reese's peanut butter cups and York peppermint candies.

Edible manufacturers have advanced their production and packaging so significantly that some companies have been subject to patent infringement lawsuits brought by the Hershey Company, the largest chocolate manufacturer in North America. Despite the threats of legal action, numerous manufacturers continue to produce edibles that look remarkably like well-known classic candy products.

One of the most popular edible manufacturers is Cheeba Chews. The company claims its edible products are available in over 800 marijuana dispensaries in the U.S. The company's product line is indicative of the future of the edibles industry. Cheeba Chews are available in a variety of dosages, containing 70 mg of THC to a whopping 175 mg of THC, and are produced from sativa, indica, and hybrid strains. The company also manufactures products made with combinations of THC and CBD, with one Cheeba Chew product providing 50 mg of CBD and a minimal, 2 mg of THC.[70]

Cakes that serve four to six people are also commercially available, with individual servings providing 25 mg of THC. These can add a certain experience to a birthday party or celebration, and it's apparent that they are probably not being manufactured, purchased, nor eaten solely for the cake's medical benefits!

When marijuana is consumed by smoking, vaping or dabbing, the cannabinoids enter the bloodstream through the lungs. The reason edibles have a different impact on users, particularly recreational uses, is that the cannabinoids make their way to the endocannabinoid system by way of the liver. Once there, THC is converted into another chemical, 11-hydroxy-THC, which is more potent, accounting for the intense psychoactive effect edible users often experience.

New York Times columnist Maureen Dowd captured national headlines with her description of her experience with edibles in her now infamous June 2, 2014, column:

The caramel-chocolate flavored candy bar looked so innocent, like the Sky Bars I used to love as a child.

Sitting in my hotel room in Denver, I nibbled off the end and then, when nothing happened, nibbled some more. I figured if I was reporting on the social revolution rocking Colorado in January, the giddy culmination of pot Prohibition, I should try a taste of legal, edible pot from a local shop.

What could go wrong with a bite or two?

Everything, as it turned out.

Not at first. For an hour, I felt nothing. I figured I'd order dinner from room service and return to my more mundane drugs of choice, chardonnay and mediocre-movies-on-demand.

But then I felt a scary shudder go through my body and brain. I barely made it from the desk to the bed, where I lay curled up in a hallucinatory state for the next eight hours. I was thirsty but couldn't move to get water. Or even turn off the lights. I was panting and paranoid, sure that when the room-service waiter knocked and I didn't answer, he'd call the police and have me arrested for being unable to handle my candy.

I strained to remember where I was or even what I was wearing, touching my green corduroy jeans and staring at the exposed-brick wall. As my paranoia deepened, I became convinced that I had died and no one was telling me.

It took all night before it began to wear off, distressingly slowly. The next day, a medical consultant at an edibles plant where I was conducting an interview mentioned that candy bars like that are supposed to be cut into 16 pieces for novices; but that recommendation hadn't been on the label.71

Although many questioned Dowd's lack of common sense, her article outlining her experience brought attention to several issues with edible marijuana products.

Despite some states seeking to mandate testing and labeling, the strength or potency of what is being ingested is an unknown. Even in states where medical or recreational cannabis have been legalized, and testing and labeling are mandated, consumers may not be ingesting what is stated on the package. While the Food and Drug Administration, (FDA) has the mandate to ensure food safety, dietary supplements and over-the-counter drugs, the FDA has so far avoided any regulation of marijuana edibles.

Adding to the confusion, even in states where medical cannabis is legal, edibles still must be produced and sold on a state-by-state basis to comply with each state's laws and regulations.

Further, because everyone's metabolism is different, marijuana has a unique impact on each user. The effect from edibles will vary based on an individual's medical diagnosis, pharmaceutical profile, size and weight, and prior or current marijuana usage.

Another issue with edibles is that unlike traditional methods of ingesting marijuana, it takes a while for the psychoactive effect, pain relief or other medical benefits to "kick in." This delay can be troublesome for uneducated consumers, as the common tendency when one "doesn't feel anything," is to eat more.

The final major concern with edibles is their appearance. Many commercially-produced edibles are manufactured to look like familiar products including Twinkies and Milky Way bars. There are also an abundance of cookbooks illustrating how to incorporate marijuana in home cooking and baking. Marijuana-infused foods that can easily be mistaken for the non-marijuana versions increase the chances that a child or unsuspecting adult might accidently eat them.

Fortunately, an overdose of marijuana is rarely, if ever, fatal, but can be scary, even for regular marijuana users. It is recommended that users who over-indulge lay down and try to relax. They will probably drift off to sleep, perhaps for up to twelve hours. When they awaken they'll typically feel rested, but typically somewhat groggy.

Efforts to standardize edible dosing continue, but a general consensus is starting to evolve. A general starting point is to ingest around 10 milligrams of THC. Typically, a relaxing and calming feeling will result, but silliness and giggles may also occur. This effect from edibles typically lasts from four to six hours.

Chapter 22: Vaping and Dabbing

"I have always loved marijuana. It has been a source of joy and comfort to me for many years. And I still think of it as a basic staple of life, along with beer and ice and grapefruits-and millions of Americans agree with me."

Hunter S. Thompson

Attend any hemp festival or Cannabis Cup, and two types of products will predominate, vaporizers and dab rigs.[1] Both share one characteristic, they heat -- without burning -- the plant material or the concentrates. When cannabis users seek to consume marijuana in the safest way possible, vaping and dabbing are often at the top of their lists.

Vaping and dabbing rely on heat. The key is what happens to the concentrate when it is heated. The difference between vaporization and dabbing is the difference between conductive and convective heating.

Dabbing and vaporization represent two competing visions for the future of consuming marijuana. Both are used for recreational purposes. Vaping is also used by many patients

---

[1] Part trade show and part festival, Cannabis Cups include judged competitions for cannabis products.

seeking an alternative to smoking because it a safer way to ingest marijuana

Vaporization or Vaping

Vaporizers provide a smokeless way to ingest marijuana and are growing in popularity. The devices incorporate a conduction or convection heating element. The air surrounding the plant material or the concentrate is heated to a high-enough temperature to cause the essential oils to boil, but not combust. This process creates a vapor that can be inhaled, providing the user with the same effect as smoking, but without the harmful carcinogens and other toxins resulting from combustion. Vaporizers can be used with the buds of a marijuana plant or a variety of concentrates.

Since it is smokeless, vaping provides a healthier alternative to smoking. There is only a minimal odor, which dissipates quickly. Many consumers prefer vaping to edibles since vaping is a sugar-free, zero-calorie way to ingest marijuana.

The efficiency of vaporizers is improving due to advances in technology. Hundreds of different vaporizers are now on the market, ranging in size from portable hand-held devices designed for plant material, to larger "coffee table" units designed for group use.

One of the most popular types of vaporizers are vape pens, which are similar to electronic cigarettes. Many are pocket sized, designed for use at sports events or concerts and are rechargeable, many by using a standard USB mobile phone charger. Vape pens are a discrete and convenient way to ingest marijuana.

Dabbing

A "dab" is a small amount of a concentrated marijuana extract, which is typically heated on the head of a titanium nail with a blowtorch. This vaporizes the extract. So if you're at a party, and someone pulls out a blowtorch, it's not necessarily a reason to run for the door, it's just dabbing.

Dabbing's growing popularity is primarily due to the intense high that it produces. Dabs are one of the fastest and most efficient ways to get very high, very quickly.

Not everyone is happy about the increased popularity of dabbing. Concerns have been voiced by many in the pro-legalization movement that the image of dabbing is detrimental to their efforts. Glass bongs and oddly-named substances being heated with blowtorches have led to comparisons with crack, the dangerous cocaine derivative.

There are other downsides to dabbing. When the titanium nail is heated by a butane torch, the temperature can near 1000 degrees. Combustion occurs when the marijuana oil hits the nail and with it smoke and all the health concerns associated with smoke.

Another downside for the novice is the concentrates typically used for dabbing tend to be extracted from very high THC marijuana strains. This high-potency combined with the immediate high can lead to a very uncomfortable psychoactive experience. Passing out is not uncommon.

Chapter 23: Capsules, Topicals, and Tinctures

"I don't think (pot) is more dangerous than alcohol."

Barack Obama

In states that have legalized medical or recreational marijuana, it is increasingly common to find capsules, topicals, and tinctures available for sale in retail stores and dispensaries. For patients who want to avoid smoking marijuana or ingesting edibles, obtaining the medical benefits of marijuana through capsules, pills and tinctures are good alternatives.

CBD-based products manufactured from concentrates containing no THC, or just trace amounts of THC can be purchased from online retailers, including Amazon. Capsules, topicals, and tinctures that include THC and CBD can only be produced and sold in states where retail or medical marijuana is legal, and then only from state-licensed retails stores or dispensaries.

Capsules, topicals, and tinctures are available in a variety of formulations. Most indicate on their packaging the percentages of THC, CBD, sometimes CBN and other cannabinoids, and the amount per dose or capsule.

139

Similar to issues with edibles and all types of extracts, there is no assurance that what the capsules, tinctures and topicals contain are what is stated on the product's label.

It is important to understand that the FDA has not approved any of these marijuana-based medicinal products for any specific medical conditions or disorders. However, the same can be said of many non-marijuana based nutraceuticals, herbal medicines and health supplements

Capsules

Capsules are often formulated for specific medical conditions. They are commonly used for inflammation, sleep and pain relief. Some formulations are produced with a higher percentage of THC for nighttime use and a lesser percentage for daytime use. Some capsules may indicate the specific strain used in their production.

Tinctures

Marijuana-based tinctures or liquids were a standard American medicine in the late 1800s and early 1900s. Tinctures typically consisted of a marijuana concentrate mixed with alcohol.

Today's tinctures are available in a variety of formulations, from high levels of THC and low levels of CBD to 100 percent CBD and no THC. Many also include some of other cannabinoids, including CBN.

Typically, a few drops of a tincture are squirted under the tongue. Many are available in a single-dose applicator bottle, or a regular dropper-topped bottle.

The use of tinctures for specific medical conditions came to the national forefront thanks to the Colorado-based Stanley Brothers, their non-profit, Realm of Caring, and their tincture, Charlotte's Web.

Charlotte's Web is a marijuana strain that was bred for its high CBD and low THC content. It was named for the six-year-old, Charlotte Figi, who suffered from Dravet Syndrome, a protracted form of epilepsy. Charlotte's success in using tinctures made from high CBD level marijuana to control her seizures was featured on Dr. Sanjay Gupta's first Weed special on CNN.

Topicals

Topicals produced from cannabinoid extracts are available as creams, lotions or salves. They are applied directly on the skin and are absorbed through the skin. Topicals are available as lotions or creams, and also as long-lasting transdermal patches.

There are different topical formulations for different purposes. They can provide localized pain relief, a reduction in soreness, or a reduction in inflammation.

Similar to marijuana concentrates available in capsule form, topicals are also available in a variety of formulations, including, high THC and low CBD, to low CBD and high THC. Some contain CBD only. Others contain other cannabinoids, including CBG or CBN. Topicals also frequently contain essential oils and can also contain clove, aloe, wintergreen, and coconut oil.

Anecdotal evidence indicates that topicals may provide benefits for patients suffering from dermatitis, arthritis, psoriasis and itching.

Topicals are a great alternative for patients who want the therapeutic benefit of marijuana, without the psychoactive effect.

PART FIVE: Marijuana-based Medicine

JEFFREY FRIEDLAND

Chapter 24: Marijuana, Exiting the Shadows and Once Again Becoming Medicine after 80 Years

"We have been terribly and systemically misled for seventy years in the United States."

Dr. Sanjay Gupta

It is 2015 and America's eight-decade-long prohibition of marijuana is finally being reexamined. As more states legalize cannabis for medical or recreational use, the pressure for solid scientific evidence of the plant's efficacy has increased. Scientists, medical practitioners, and patients are lobbying for scientific, clinical trials.

Unfortunately, marijuana is still classified as a Schedule I substance by the U.S. government. This places it in the same category as heroin and indicates that it carries significant risk but no known medical benefits.

Consistent with marijuana's Schedule I status, the United States Drug Enforcement Administration stands firm in its position that marijuana has "no currently accepted medical treatment use," and that it has a "lack of accepted safety for use."

This absurd statement flies in the face of the international research that is ongoing in countries including Israel, Canada, and the United Kingdom.

Adding insult to injury is that U.S. law empowers the National Institute on Drug Abuse, NIDA, with oversight of all narcotics as defined by the Controlled Substances Act. NIDA is the only legal supplier of marijuana for research purposes in the U.S., the perfect example of a "fox guarding the hen house."

Research institutions interested in marijuana research must first obtain approval from the FDA. If approved, marijuana can then only be obtained from NIDA's grow facility in Mississippi. This facility has had very limited supplies of marijuana, but it's production has increased.

That being said, it is widely acknowledged that the extremely limited selection of marijuana grown by the U.S. government is grossly inferior to the many strains grown in states that have legalized marijuana. With the tremendous potential of CBD-based medical marijuana, the U.S. government's Mississippi grow facility is particularly lacking in marijuana strains that are high in CBD and low in THC.

There is vast anecdotal evidence indicating marijuana's usefulness in treating a variety of physical and psychological conditions. However, U.S. studies are lacking to prove the benefit of medical marijuana for any condition or disease.[I] This lack of scientific research is both perplexing and frustrating because the safety and efficacy will ultimately determine the future of marijuana-based medicine.

Finally, in 2013, the first clinical trials under FDA protocols were initiated for Epidiolex, a pure form of CBD in liquid form that contains no THC.[II] The objective of these trials was to

---

[I] Anecdotal evidence is based on reports of isolated or unique observations. Evidence based on anecdotes arises from the analysis of individual clinical cases, rather than the study of scientifically randomized groups of patients. Anecdotal evidence may be true or false, but is scientifically unreliable.

[II] Epidiolex was developed by UK-based GW Pharmaceuticals.

evaluate the effectiveness of the drug in treating forms of childhood epilepsy in those patients who have not responded to standard antiepileptic drugs.

The Obama administration slightly streamlined the approval process for clinical trials in 2014. It made it marginally easier for researchers to obtain permission for studies, but securing approval is still a significant regulatory and bureaucratic quagmire.

There has been speculation that the "Big Pharma" lobby has been a primary driver in keeping marijuana illegal. Conspiracy theorists believe that the pharmaceutical industry's motivation is to protect their pharmaceuticals from competitive marijuana-based medicines. The facts and general consensus indicate that this is not the case.

The pharmaceutical industry has limited interest in researching marijuana-based medicine because of the difficulty in protecting the intellectual property of any discovery that is made. Obtaining a patent for drugs produced from natural plants is nearly impossible. Also, the U.S. Patent and Trademark Office will not issue patents for marijuana-based medicine as long as it is illegal federally.

The pharmaceutical industry has developed synthetic cannabinoids that directly activate endocannabinoid system receptors. However, there is evidence that whole-plant cannabinoids derived from the marijuana plant are more effective than cannabinoids that have been synthesized in a laboratory. This is described as the whole-plant or entourage effect.

There are numerous unknowns and concerns related to the development of whole-plant cannabis-based medicine, for both patients and physicians. One of the most significant is what the appropriate percentages of CBD, THC, and other cannabinoids are that are most beneficial for specific diseases and conditions. Current dosages for specific medical conditions and ratios of cannabinoids to body mass are more art than science and the dearth of clinical and scientific research does not serve the patient well.

The consistency of formulations is also of concern. Is what the patient believes is being ingested, what is being ingested?

Questions have also been raised about the optimal delivery method for specific diseases or conditions. Science is lacking as to whether ingesting oils, eating edibles, smoking, vaping, or a liquid tincture is best.

The cannabis industry is in its infancy. It is the Wild West. Caveat emptor, or let the buyer beware, is the message. Although there are numerous studies, websites, reference materials and forums that provide patients with the ability to research their specific medical conditions and the applicability of marijuana-based medicine, the question of validity always looms in the background.

Despite all the obstacles and unknowns, many patients are not waiting for science, Congress, regulators or bureaucrats to clear the way. Tens of thousands of Americans are using marijuana for medical purposes. Parents of children with Dravet syndrome are moving thousands of miles to states that have legalized marijuana hoping that they can obtain medicine that will alleviate their child's seizures. Cancer patients are using medical marijuana to address side effects of chemotherapy, including nausea. Soldiers returning home to the U.S. from combat duty are self-treating with marijuana for their symptoms of Post-Traumatic Stress Disorder, PTSD.

Chapter 25: Israel's History and Role in Marijuana Research

The State of Israel is a dynamic global leader in a number of industries. These include innovations in the biotechnology and technology sectors, the country's role as a leader in sophisticated security systems, and its agricultural innovations, which have allowed the country to thrive by making the desert bloom.

Israel's focus on agriculture and biotech provided the perfect platform for marijuana research. Marijuana is illegal for recreational use in Israel but has been available for research since the 1990s. The country's Ministry of Health, the equivalent of the U.S. Food and Drug Administration has publicly acknowledged that there are medical benefits from marijuana.

Israeli marijuana growers have leveraged the expertise developed in plant sciences over the decades, and transferred that knowledge to the breeding and growing of medical-grade marijuana.

Research in Israel into the biochemistry of biologically active compounds in marijuana has a long history.

Israel's role as the world leader in marijuana research is due to the persistence and perseverance of Dr. Raphael Mechoulam.

149

As a chemist at the Hebrew University of Jerusalem in the early 1960s, Mechoulam and his colleagues conducted numerous studies that established the foundation for the entire field of marijuana science.

It was Roger Adams, at the University of Illinois, who first isolated cannabidiol or CBD in 1940. At the time of Adams' discovery, the technology did not exist to determine CBD's exact chemical structure. It was Mechoulam and his colleague, Yuval Shvo, who uncovered CBD's chemical structure in 1962.

A year later, Mechoulam and Yehiel Gaoni became the first scientists to isolate THC, the main active compound in marijuana and the one responsible for the plant's psychoactive effects.

It took another thirty years, until 1992, for Mechoulam, Bill Devane, and Lumir Hanus to discover the brain's first endogenous cannabinoid. Mechoulam explanation included the statement:

a receptor in the body does not exist because there is a plant out there...we decided that the body has to have compounds that activate this receptor.

Mechoulam and his colleagues were relatively sure that humans had selective receptors in their bodies that allowed cannabinoids in marijuana to bind to them.

Mechoulam's team discovered endocannabinoids, a compound in the human body that activates cannabinoid receptors. The researchers dubbed it Anandamide, which in Sanskrit means "supreme joy." Two years later they discovered a second endogenous compound.

This discovery of the endocannabinoid system revitalized the interest in marijuana research and revolutionized the way scientists studied the relationship between marijuana and the human body.

Researchers began to focus on discovering how the endocannabinoids produced by the human body, and cannabinoids found in the marijuana plant, could be modified for different receptors. This new research approach was monumental, as it had the potential of providing treatments for dozens of diseases and medical conditions.

Mechoulam's research was the precursor for Israel's Ministry of Health approving the use of marijuana for a vast number of medical conditions in 2007. These included certain types of cancer, epilepsy, neurological disorders, multiple sclerosis, Parkinson's disease and Tourette syndrome.

As of 2015, seven Israeli growers provide more than 50 marijuana strains for patients, which are distributed via dispensaries located throughout the country.

Studies in Israel have investigated the use of marijuana-based medicine in the treatment of basal-cell carcinoma, post-traumatic stress disorder or PTSD, fibromyalgia and Crohn's disease. Some of this research is ongoing.

Israel's marijuana research has attracted scientists and researchers from all over the world who are seeking to take advantage of the country's medical marijuana-friendly laws.

One of those researchers was Dr. Sue Sisley, an Arizona-based physician. She received U.S. government approval to test marijuana on American veterans suffering from post-traumatic stress disorder or PTSD. She stated that she traveled to Israel to have, "access to strains of marijuana that we weren't able to obtain from our own federal government."

Marijuana research in Israel is continuing with companies developing cannabinoid-based treatments, advanced marijuana breeding technologies, and alternative delivery methods including metered dose inhalers.

Research into Marijuana as a Cancer Treatment

Perhaps Israel's most exciting marijuana research was initiated at the Technion-Israel Institute of Technology in Haifa, where marijuana is being investigated as a potential treatment against the development of cancer itself.

One of the primary characteristics of cancer cells is their aggressive multiplication and ability to avoid the normal mechanisms of death. Israeli researchers were successful in causing brain cancer cells to essentially, "commit suicide," what is referred to as apoptosis, a type of programmed cell death. The conclusion is that marijuana somehow succeeds in initiating this death mechanism in cancer cells, but researchers do not yet understand how this occurs.

This research in Israel is the first attempt at using marijuana as a cancer treatment. The goal is to examine whether the plant might be beneficial in delaying the development of cancer cells or eliminating the cells completely.

Led by Dr. David Meiri, the head of the Technion's Laboratory of Cancer Biology and Cannabinoid Research, the initial focus was to evaluate dozens of marijuana strains to determine if they affected the development and growth of hundreds of types of cancer cells.

Preliminary research results were announced in 2015 and indicated a potential for treating brain and breast cancers. Although very preliminary, these results sparked great interest and a clamoring for additional research within the cancer research community.

This research, which as of the writing of this book during the fall of 2015, is ongoing, is also investigating other therapeutic agents in the marijuana plant.

Israeli scientists at the Technion believe that terpenoids and flavonoids, which are present in small quantities in marijuana, may also have beneficial therapeutic effects and may operate synergistically with specific cannabinoids.[1]

---

[1]Terpenoids, are a large and diverse class of naturally occurring organic chemicals similar to terpenes. Terpenoids derived from plants are used extensively for their aromatic qualities and are prevalent in herbal remedies.

Flavonoids are a group of plant metabolites found in a variety of plants, including common fruits and vegetables. Evidence indicates that flavonoids provide health benefits through cell signaling pathways and that they provide antioxidant effects. They are responsible for the vibrant color of many foods. Foods with a high flavonoid content include onions, parsley, blueberries and other berries, bananas, all citrus fruits and some dark chocolate.

JEFFREY FRIEDLAND

Chapter 26: The Key to Marijuana-Based Medicine: The Human Endocannabinoid System

"The science is there. This isn't anecdotal."

Dr. Sanjay Gupta

The revolutionary discovery of the endocannabinoid system in Israel in 1992 accelerated the understanding of the way human cells communicate. It led to a reinvestigation of the interactions of plant and synthetic cannabinoids with the human endocannabinoid system and other biochemical entities.[72]

Endocannabinoid receptors, CB_1, and CB_2 are at the foundation of this system and are found throughout the body. They provide broad influence over sensations including pain perception, movement, emotion, cognition, and sleep.

CB_1 receptors control neurons that are most prevalent in the central and peripheral nervous system, the ganglia and nerves located outside of the brain and spinal cord. CB_1 receptors are also present in the lungs, liver, and kidneys. Interestingly, CB_1 receptors are not present in the medulla oblongata, which is the part of the brain stem responsible for cardiovascular and respiratory functions.

CB_2 receptors are present in the peripheral nervous system, in the immune system, and are highly concentrated in the spleen and liver.

Both CB_1 and CB_2 receptors can be activated by the body's own endogenous cannabinoids, natural chemical compounds that are normally created by the body. These are referred to as endocannabinoids. Exogenous cannabinoids, those found in the marijuana plant, provide medical benefits by binding with or blocking these CB_1 or CB_2 receptors.

One way to think about the endocannabinoid system is as a system of locks and keys. Receptors can be thought of as the locks and cannabinoids as the keys. When the right "key" or cannabinoid finds the matching "lock" or receptor, the equivalent of a door is opened and a message is delivered.

Many of the therapeutic functions of the endocannabinoid system are well known and documented and research is ongoing.

The cannabinoids in marijuana and their activation of these receptors indicate potential in fighting tumors, autoimmune disorders and serious neurological conditions for which treatment options are limited or non-existent. Early-stage research indicates that the cannabinoids in marijuana have a strong anti-inflammatory effect because of the CB_2 receptors, and are beneficial as painkillers because of the CB_1 receptors.

The Concept of an Endocannabinoid Deficiency

The discovery of the endocannabinoid system provided new insights into the possibility of treatments for a wide variety of previously intractable disorders. This has led to a hypothesis that many medical conditions may result from an endocannabinoid deficiency.

Every neurotransmitter system has conditions attributable to a deficiency. These include dementia in patients suffering from

Alzheimer disease due to loss of acetylcholine activity, Parkinson's due to a deficiency of dopamine, and depression due to lowered levels of serotonin, norepinephrine or other amines. It has been theorized that a similar deficiency may exist for the endocannabinoid system, whose receptor density is greater than many of the human body's other neurotransmitter systems.

The concept of a Clinical Endocannabinoid Deficiency, or CECD, may help explain various medical conditions. These include pathophysiology headaches, fibromyalgia, and irritable bowel syndrome and related disorders.

One of the most interesting areas of CEDC research is Post Traumatic Stress Disorder, which is increasingly associated with a dysfunctional endocannabinoid system.

JEFFREY FRIEDLAND

Chapter 27: Cannabidiol or CBD, a Medical Game Changer

"Hemp is of first necessity to the wealth and protection of the country."

Thomas Jefferson

Cannabidiol or CBD is one of the 111 known cannabinoids in cannabis. CBD is produced by all cannabis plants, including marijuana and industrial hemp.

Although the hemp plant only contains trace amounts of the psychoactive cannabinoid THC, the U.S. government considers it to be the same plant as marijuana, thus it is also a Schedule I drug under the Controlled Substances Act.

Charlotte's Web

Six-year-old Charlotte Figi suffered from Dravet syndrome, a severe form of epilepsy, marked by intractable seizure activity. By age three, Charlotte was severely disabled, having up to 300 grand mal seizures weekly. Treatment with conventionally-prescribed pharmaceuticals for Dravet syndrome did not help her condition.

Charlotte's parents were desperate to find a treatment for her epilepsy. Her parents learned about another child with Dravet syndrome, who had experienced success in using a marijuana-based oil. They wanted the same oil for Charlotte.

The Figis began working with Colorado physician, Dr. Alan Shackelford, who believed that CBD was a viable option for Charlotte. Shackelford recommended it despite his concerns about a child using marijuana.

In 2011, Charlotte was given an oil-based marijuana extract in the form of a tincture, manufactured by the Colorado-based Stanley brothers. The Stanley brothers had cross-bred a strain of marijuana with a strain of industrial hemp creating a new strain with significantly less THC and more CBD than typical marijuana strains.

Within a short period of time Charlotte's condition significantly improved. Her parents reported that her seizures dropped from hundreds per month to about four per month.

The Stanley brothers named their new strain Charlotte's Web in honor of Charlotte. The brothers claimed that Charlotte's Web had the highest amount of CBD in the world, approximating 20 percent and a minimal amount, .05 percent of THC.

Her treatment garnered national attention when her parents revealed that they obtained medical marijuana to treat her condition. Dr. Sanjay Gupta, CNN's Chief Medical Correspondent, and a neurosurgeon, highlighted Charlotte, her parents and Dr. Shackelford in his first CNN special report, *Weed*, which aired in August 2013. Before meeting Charlotte and her parents, Gupta had been critical of the use of medical cannabis. Regarding his change in the use of marijuana-based medicine, Gupta stated:

> *I apologize because I didn't look hard enough, until now. I didn't look far enough. I didn't review papers from smaller labs in other countries doing some remarkable research, and I was too dismissive of the loud chorus of legitimate patients whose symptoms improved on cannabis.*

They didn't have the science to support that claim, and I now know that when it comes to marijuana neither of those things are true. It doesn't have a high potential for abuse, and there are very legitimate medical applications. In fact, sometimes marijuana is the only thing that works. Take the case of Charlotte Figi, who I met in Colorado. She started having seizures soon after birth. By age 3, she was having 300 a week, despite being on seven different medications. Medical marijuana has calmed her brain, limiting her seizures to 2 or 3 per month.

We have been terribly and systematically misled for nearly 70 years in the United States, and I apologize for my own role in that.

The results that Charlotte had in taking a high-CBD tincture were again featured the following year in CNN's *Weed 2: Cannabis Madness*. Charlotte's experience in benefiting from marijuana-based medicine is credited by many as the primary catalyst for many states changing their laws to allow medical marijuana.

Similar to many other experimental marijuana therapies, there were no clinical trials for Charlotte's Web, nor had it been approved by the Food and Drug Administration for patients with Dravet Syndrome, or any other medical condition or disease. The success that Charlotte and other children suffering from Dravet syndrome seizures obtained from a marijuana-based medicine is considered anecdotal.

The publicity surrounding Charlotte Figi's tremendous success in being treated with a high-CBD strain of marijuana precipitated other parents and their children relocating to Colorado from all over the U.S. There have been mixed results for children taking Charlotte's Web, again reinforcing the need for clinical trials for Dravet syndrome and other medical conditions.

Medical Benefits of CBD

Early-stage research suggests that CBD may provide many medicinal benefits without the psychoactive effects caused by THC. There are indications that CBD, without THC, can help control seizures, lower anxiety and even reduce the size of some cancerous tumors.

161

Essentially all evidence regarding the validity of CBD-based medicine is considered anecdotal. This includes experiences that physicians have observed from their patients' use of CBD-based formulations, or from the experience of budtenders and herbal medicine practitioners based on the direct feedback from patients. Despite the lack of scientific evidence, it is impossible to ignore what are likely the significant potential benefits from CBD-based medicine.

Before the phenomenal results for some children suffering from Dravet syndrome from Charlotte's Web, low-CBD strains of marijuana were deemed of little value by growers. There was no demand for low-THC marijuana strains for recreational use. Initially called, "Hippies Disappointment," low-THC marijuana was dismissed as hemp, which is legally-defined in the U.S. as a marijuana plant having a THC content of less than 0.3 percent.

All of this changed with Charlotte's Web. Industrial hemp was seen by many as a perfect source of CBD.

Products produced from the stalk or seeds of industrial hemp could be legally imported into the United States. Many of these products were imported from China, Canada, the Czech Republic, Germany and the United Kingdom. These included hemp seed oil, hemp seeds and fabric and clothing derived from hemp. Some product labels state that they contain CBD, some do not.

If the products that are labeled hemp seed oil or hemp oil, have any significant amount of CBD, it has to be derived from the bud and flowers surrounding the bud, and not the stalk or seeds. Because of this, it's questionable if there is CBD in many of the products manufactured from imported hemp.

Once CBD became known for its medicinal properties, the interest in cultivating hemp in the United States as an agricultural crop significantly increased. Because it was illegal to grow industrial hemp in the United States until President Obama signed the Agricultural Act of 2014, most CBD-based medical formulations were from the marijuana plant, not from industrial hemp.

The Agricultural Act of 2014 only allowed the growing of industrial hemp in the U.S. for research and development purposes under the purview of state agricultural departments that had a registration process. It did not allow for commercial growing. Despite this commercial prohibition, the growing of industrial hemp for commercial purposes is underway in many states. The general consensus is that since industrial hemp only contains trace amounts of THC, that hemp is not an enforcement priority for the Drug Enforcement Administration.

Following in the footsteps of the Stanley brothers, other marijuana breeders developed varieties of high-CBD, low-HTC marijuana. Two of these are the California-developed marijuana strains, AC DC and Ringo's Gift. Breeders in Israel have developed a high CBD strain, which they named Avidekel. It contains no THC and its buds contain 15 to 16 percent CBD.

As this book is being written during the fall of 2015, there are now numerous CBD-based formulations available in the U.S. that derived from American grown industrial hemp and not marijuana.

Ruth Gallily, a researcher at the Hebrew University in Jerusalem, who studied CBD for more than 12 years, said she has found that CBD derived from low-THC marijuana plants as having impressive anti-inflammatory qualities.[73] She stated:

The cannabis plant, enriched with CBD, can be used for treating diseases like rheumatoid arthritis, heart disease, and diabetes.[74]

The first U.S. clinical trials for a CBD-based pharmaceutical, or for that matter for any marijuana-based medicine, were approved by the Food and Drug Administration in 2013. These multi-center, clinical trials were initiated by United Kingdom-based GW Pharmaceuticals for its drug, Epidiolex, as a potential treatment for pediatric epilepsy disorders. It has been suggested that Epidiolex could be approved by the FDA and available for patients in 2016.

JEFFREY FRIEDLAND

Chapter 28: Medical Benefits from the Other Cannabinoids

In addition to the best-known cannabinoids THC and CBD, there is evidence that some of the 109 other cannabinoids in the marijuana plant also provide medical benefits.

Anecdotal evidence has been provided by budtenders in dispensaries, online reports and by alternative healthcare providers. No clinical trials have determined the efficacy, dosage or best method of ingestion of any of these other cannabinoids.

Cannabidiolic Acid or CBDA

Cannabidiolic acid or CBDA is a compound in marijuana or hemp plants with high levels of CBD. There are indications that CBDA selectively inhibits the cyclooxygenase enzyme, COX-2, which is found at sites of inflammation and contributes to the generally acknowledged anti-inflammatory properties of marijuana. CBDA has also been described as having antibiotic properties that are similar to penicillin.

Cannabinol or CBN

Cannabinol or CBN is a mildly-psychoactive cannabinoid which is formed during the degradation of THC. There is very little CBN in a freshly-harvested marijuana plant.

There is evidence that CBN acts as a weak agonist, a chemical that activates a biological response, at both the CB_1 and CB_2 receptors, with CBN having a greater affinity for the CB_2 receptor. The degradation of THC into CBN has been shown to enhance the effects of THC, resulting in a sedative effective.

Cannabigerol or CBG

Cannabigerol or CBG is a non-psychoactive cannabinoid, which research indicates may have benefits as an antibacterial agent. Preliminary studies have shown that it may kill or slow bacterial growth, reduce inflammation, especially in its acidic CBGA form, inhibit cell growth in tumor and cancer cells, and promote bone growth.

Cannabichromene or CBC

Cannabichromene or CBC is more common in tropically-grown varieties of marijuana. Studies have shown that CBC can be effective as an analgesic to reduce inflammation, that it can inhibit cell growth in tumor and cancer cells, and that it is beneficial in promoting bone growth.

Cannabidivarin or CBDV

Very little is known about how cannabidivarin or CBDV provides medical benefits. Studies have indicated promise for its use in the management of epilepsy.

Tetrahydrocannabivarin or THCV

Tetrahydrocannabivarin or THCV is a minor cannabinoid that is not found in all cannabis strains. Preliminary research indicates that THCV may be effective in reducing panic attacks, as an appetite suppressor and that it may be beneficial in the promotion of bone growth.

Tetrahydrocananbinolic Acid or THCA

THCA is the main chemical compound in freshly-harvested marijuana. It converts to THC when heated, burned or vaporized.

Along with CBDA, CBGA, and other acidic cannabinoids, THCA contains the two cyclooxygenase enzymes, COX-1, and COX-2, which evidence indicates provide some of the anti-inflammatory properties of marijuana.[1] COX-2 dominates at sites of inflammation and COX-1 acts to speed up the production of certain chemical messengers and prostaglandins, in areas of the body including the stomach and kidneys. In the stomach, COX-1 promotes the production of a protective natural mucus lining.

Early-stage research also indicates that THCA interacts with certain cells that cause inflammation and other conditions. THCA may be beneficial as an anti-proliferative, a substance that prevents or retards the spread and growth of cells, especially preventing the spread of malignant cells into surrounding tissues; and as an antispasmodic, a substance that prevents or relieves spasms or convulsions.

While marijuana-based medicine is available in states where medical marijuana is legal, the ability to obtain medicines based on these minor-cannabinoids is very limited. Most growers or extractors do not have the education, skills nor equipment to isolate these individual cannabinoids. It is currently very difficult for patients to try marijuana-based medicine formulated from these lesser cannabinoids. The availability of formulations based on these minor cannabinoids will likely increase in the coming years.

---

[1] Cyclooxygenase (COX), officially known as prostaglandin-endoperoxide synthase (PTGS), is an enzyme that is responsible for the formation of prostanoids, fatty acid derivatives, often present in tiny concentrations that research indicates have profound effects on cellular physiological and pathophysiological reactions. It has two forms, COX-1 and COX-2.

JEFFREY FRIEDLAND

Chapter 29: The Entourage or Whole Plant Effect

Along with his discoveries related to cannabis and its medical benefits, Mechoulam made many other contributions to the understanding of the plant's interaction with the human body. In a 1998 paper, he discussed the benefit of utilizing the whole plant in addition to specific compounds:[75]

> There are more than 480 natural components found within the cannabis plant, of which 111 are classified as cannabinoids. The other known constituents of the cannabis plant are 27 nitrogenous compounds, 18 amino acids, 3 proteins, 6 glycoproteins, 2 enzymes, 34 sugars and related compounds, 50 hydrocarbons, 7 simple alcohols, 13 aldehydes, 13 ketones, 21 simple acids, 22 fatty acids, 12 simple esters, 1 lactone, 11 steroids, 120 terpenes, 25 non-cannabinoid phenols, 21 flavonoids, 1 vitamins, 2 pigments, and 9 other elements.[76]

Mechoulam, along with other researchers, believes that all these components of the cannabis plant likely exert some therapeutic effect, more than any single compound by itself.

Science has not yet identified the exact role or mechanism for these various compounds, but the evidence is mounting that they work better together than in isolation. This hypothesis is described as the "entourage effect."

Synthetic Cannabinoids in Comparison to Natural Cannabinoids Produced from Plants

Cannabinoids, as chemical compounds, can be synthetically produced. Preliminary research indicates that medicine produced from the marijuana plant are more effective than synthetically produced individual cannabinoid compounds. The hypothesis is that this is a result of the entourage effect.

One example is synthetically-produced THC, which is marketed under the brand name Marinol. Patients in hospitals are often given Marinol as an alternative to opiate pain-killers. Anecdotal evidence indicates that Marinol is not as effective as a painkiller as high-THC medicine derived from the marijuana plant.

The validity of the entourage effect was proven by research completed in Israel in 2015. The research concluded that CBD extracted from a marijuana plant had superior therapeutic properties to synthetically manufactured, single-molecule CBD.[77] The Israeli study indicated that medicine derived from the plant "is superior over (synthetically produced) CBD for the treatment of inflammatory conditions."

A conclusion of the research was that the greater efficacy of an extract derived from the "whole plant" was likely the result of interactions between CBD and dozens of the minor cannabinoids and perhaps hundreds of other non-cannabinoid compounds. The report stated:

A lot of research has been made to isolate and characterize isolated single constituents of traditional herbal medicine to find their rationale for therapeutic uses..."[78]

The conclusion of the report was:

However, our data together with those of others provide legitimation to introduce a new generation of phytopharmaceuticals to treat diseases that have hitherto been treated using synthetic drugs alone. The therapeutic synergy observed with plant extracts results in the requirement for a lower amount of active components, with consequent reduced adverse effects.[79]

This research countered the position taken by many scientists and members of the drug industry that "crude" herbal medicines made from the marijuana plant are low-grade and low quality, compared to the pure, single molecule compounds that could be synthetically manufactured in a laboratory.

Israeli scientists concluded that the plant-based medicine is superior to synthesized cannabinoids.

JEFFREY FRIEDLAND

Chapter 30: Benefits of Marijuana-Based Medicine for Chronic Pain and Inflammation

Marijuana has been used for medicinal purposes for thousands of years. Cynics point to the lack of formal scientific evidence regarding its efficacy, but it is difficult to dispute the vast amount of anecdotal evidence supporting the medical benefits of the plant.

Currently, there is only one clinical trial that has been initiated in the United States under the auspices of the Food and Drug Administration. That trial is for the drug Epidiolex, a pure form of cannabidiol or CBD, in a liquid form that contains no THC. There are other companies, research firms, and universities preparing to submit proposals for studies to the FDA. Hopefully, as the legal barriers are eliminated, research will lead to "real marijuana-based medicine, based on real science."

The two most significant applications for the use of marijuana-based medicine are for pain and inflammation. Chronic pain and inflammation are pervasive across most illnesses and conditions and often the most debilitating for patients. Both interfere with the quality of life and the ability to function on a daily basis.

Marijuana-based medicine appears to work for humans because of our CB1 and CB2 receptors. In addition to the minor cannabinoids, preliminary research indicates that THC has the greatest impact on CB_1 receptors for pain, and CBD has the greatest impact on the CB_2 receptors for inflammation.

Marijuana-Based Medicine as a Treatment for Chronic Pain

In economically advanced countries, pain is the most common reason for visiting a doctor. More than 76 million Americans suffer from chronic pain, more people than diabetes, heart disease, and cancer combined.[80] Chronic pain is one of the most common conditions for which patients seek to use marijuana-based medicine, and the evidence of its effectiveness is fairly compelling. The International Association for Cannabinoid Medicines' *Database for Clinical Studies* lists more than 100 studies completed or in progress on the use of marijuana for pain.[81]

Pain experts have divided the physical causes of pain into two types, nociceptive and neuropathic pain. The differences are important for understanding the nature of the pain problem and especially for the establishment of a treatment protocol.

Nociceptors are the nerves which sense and respond to parts of the body which suffer from damage. They signal tissue irritation, impending injury, or actual injury. When activated, they transmit pain signals, via the peripheral nerves as well as the spinal cord, to the brain. Nociceptive pain tends to cease once the body is healed.

Nociceptive pain is generally associated with a specific injury or from arthritis. Examples of nociceptive pain include sprains, bone fractures, burns, and lacerations. It tends to respond well to treatment with opioids.

Neuropathic pain is the result of an injury or malfunction in the peripheral or central nervous system. The pain is often triggered by an injury, but this injury may or may not involve actual

174

damage to the nervous system. Nerves can be infiltrated or compressed by tumors, strangulated by scar tissue, or inflamed by infection. The pain frequently has burning, lancinating, or electric shock qualities.

Neuropathic pain may persist for months or years beyond the apparent healing of any damaged tissues, and may not be reversible. Partial improvement is often possible with proper treatment. In these cases, the pain signals no longer represents an ongoing injury, but rather an indication that the system itself is malfunctioning.

Examples of neuropathic pain include shingles, components of cancer pain, phantom limb pain, carpal tunnel syndrome and widespread nerve damage. Chronic pain may also result from conditions such as diabetes, exposure to toxins such as chemotherapy, vitamin deficiencies, and a large variety of other medical conditions. It is not unusual for the cause of the condition to go undiagnosed.

The Mayo Clinic recommends various THC-based medicines for pain. These include the synthetically produced Nabilone and Sativex. Marijuana-based THC and CBD are also recommended, smoked, in capsule form, or as a tincture, sprayed under the tongue.

Marijuana-Based Medicine for Pain as an Alternative to Opiates

The cannabinoid receptors of the endocannabinoid system are found throughout the human body. Research shows that when skin or flesh is cut or injured, endocannabinoids are released to help modulate the pain associated with the injuries. Experts believe that the endocannabinoid system may act as a biological mechanism for controlling pain in the human body, therefore, providing an opportunity for therapeutic applications based on cannabinoids.

Studies have shown that when cannabinoids bind to the receptors in nerve and brain cells, they behave as analgesics in models of both acute nociception and clinical pain including inflammation and painful neuropathy. In effect, they alter the way these cells perceive a painful stimulus, ultimately reducing the intensity of pain that is interpreted by the brain.

Opioids are the most widely prescribed treatment for pain relief. Humans have an insatiable appetite for opioids to the extent that our own brains produce them. They are called endorphins.

Long-term use of opiates is associated with serious side effects, including abuse, dependence, and even death. Opiate painkillers can also damage the lining of the gastrointestinal tract.

Unlike opiates, marijuana has no known lethal dose, minimal drug interactions, and is easily dosed via oral ingestion, vaporization, or topical absorption. The use of marijuana-based medicine, in a form other than smoking plant material, eliminates potential health risks associated with smoking.

The gastrointestinal tract is lined with CB_1 receptors, the cannabinoids may also stimulate its repair and reduce unwanted symptoms including stomach pain, food sensitivity, and diarrhea.

There is evidence that combining opiates with marijuana-based medicine might be advantageous for pain control.

A 2011 study led by Donald Abrams, professor of clinical medicine at the University of California San Francisco and chief of the Hematology-Oncology Division at the San Francisco General Hospital and Trauma Center examined the interaction between cannabinoids and opiates. This was the first human study of its kind. Abrams' team found the combination of both opiates and marijuana-based medicine reduced pain more than using opiates alone.[82]

Studies also indicate that marijuana-based medicine can prevent the development of opioid tolerance and shows promise in addressing withdrawal symptoms. It is thought that the chemicals in marijuana interrupt signals sent by the opioid receptor system.

The general conclusion is that cannabinoid-based medicines show significant promise in both relieving the suffering from chronic pain and also reduce the risk of side effects that are associated with the use of opioid medications.

Cannabis-Based Medicine as a Treatment for Inflammation

Relief from inflammation is perhaps the second most compelling reason that patients seek marijuana-based medicine. One cannabinoid, CBD, has been found to be more effective than aspirin as an anti-inflammatory agent.[83]

Inflammation is the immune system's response to infection and injury. Heat, tenderness, swelling and redness are associated with inflammation and are vital to the healing process. When the immune system is functioning properly, inflammation results in the repair of the damaged tissue, when it is not, it can cause long-term, or even permanent damage.

Inflammation is a symptom of many medical conditions and disorders. Chronic inflammation plays an important role in many debilitating ailments, including autoimmune diseases including lupus, colitis, arthritis and multiple sclerosis.

Chronic inflammation may lead to a host of diseases, including hay fever, periodontitis, atherosclerosis, rheumatoid arthritis, and cancer. It can also lead to scarring, loss of organ function and has been implicated in the progression of arthritis and cancer as well as stroke, neurodegenerative and cardiovascular diseases.

Cannabinoids via the body's CB2 receptors trigger a cascade of biochemical reactions that can help combat inflammation. Research is targeting CB2 receptors as a therapeutic strategy to prevent diseases. Crohn's disease, an inflammation of the intestinal tract, cirrhosis of the liver, osteoarthritis and atherosclerosis are among the disease being researched for their positive responses to cannabis.

Although THC also activates the CB1 and CB2 receptors and is helpful in reducing inflammation, it has the side effect of being a psychoactive agent, unlike CBD, which does not induce a "high."

THC activates both the CB_1 and CB_2 receptors so it won't alleviate inflammation without also making people high. This has increased interest among researchers on the effect of the non-psychoactive CBD on CB_2 receptors.

Research is targeting CB_2 receptors as a therapeutic strategy to prevent diseases including Crohn's disease, which is inflammation of the intestinal tract, liver cirrhosis, osteoarthritis, and atherosclerosis.

Marc Feldman, a colleague of Mechoulam's at the Imperial College in London, researched the effect of CBD on mice who had a version of rheumatoid arthritis. With the right dosage, he found that CBD reduced the mice's inflammation by 50 percent.[84]

Cardiologists at the Hebrew University in Jerusalem also conducted research with mice and found that a dosage of CBD immediately following a heart attack reduced the size of an infarct, a small localized area of dead tissue resulting from failure of the blood supply, by about 66 percent.[85]

In addition to the anti-inflammatory benefits of CBD, another cannabinoid, beta-caryophyllene, or (E)-BCP, also has been shown to be effective for inflammation in studies going back to 2008. Previously, cannabis research had primarily been focused primarily only on the cannabinoids CBD and THC.

(E)-BCP is already part of many people's daily diets. Foods that are high in (E)-BCP include black pepper, oregano, basil, lime, cinnamon, carrots, and celery. When essential oils are extracted from marijuana plants, they can contain up to 35 percent (E)-BCP.

Chapter 31: Marijuana-based Medicine for Specific Medical Conditions and Diseases

"As a physician I don't feel right in telling a patient to take two tokes and call me in the morning."

Dr. Alan Shackelford

Anecdotal evidence indicates that marijuana may provide benefit for many medical conditions and disorders beyond simply managing pain and inflammation.

Before 2014, medical marijuana research in the United States was minimal, since cultivating or using the plant was illegal under federal law. As I write this book during the fall of 2015, researching the medical benefits of marijuana has improved negligibly. Obtaining permission to initiate research is still challenging because of the bureaucratic and regulatory restrictions placed on the use of marijuana by the federal government.

Research into the benefits of medical marijuana is in its very early stages. The information that follows regarding medical conditions and disorders which may benefit from the use of marijuana is largely based on anecdotal patient experiences. It is

179

important to understand that none of these references to the use of medical marijuana have been approved by the Food and Drug Administration.

Hopefully, in the coming years there will be valid clinical data supporting many of the benefits of marijuana-based medicine, including those that follow.

Acne and Skin Disorders

Acne is a skin condition that occurs when hair follicles become plugged with oil and dead skin cells. Acne usually appears on the face, neck, chest, back and shoulders. Effective treatments are available, but acne can be persistent. Acne is most common among teenagers, but younger children and adults can suffer as well. Depending on its severity, acne can cause emotional distress and scar the skin.[86]

Scientists from Hungary, Germany, and the United Kingdom discovered that endocannabinoids play an important role in maintaining healthy skin and treating skin conditions ranging from acne to dry skin, and even skin-related tumors.

Early-stage research indicates that the main physiological function of the endocannabinoid system as it affects the skin is to control the proper and well-balanced proliferation, differentiation, and survival, as well as immune competence and tolerance of skin cells. It is thought that the disruption of this delicate balance might facilitate the development of multiple pathological conditions and diseases of the skin, including acne, seborrhea, allergic dermatitis, itch and pain, psoriasis, hair growth disorders, systemic sclerosis and cancer.[87]

A 2014 study published in the Journal of Clinical Investigation explored the effects of the endocannabinoid system in the regulation of multiple physiological processes, including cutaneous cell growth and differentiation.

The report indicated that CBD is a potent and "universal" anti-acne agent, possessing a unique "triple anti-acne" profile, and points to marijuana as a promising, cost-effective, and, likely, well-tolerated new strategy for treating acne vulgaris, the most common human skin disease.[88]

The Mayo Clinic recommends a formulation of hemp seed oil, taken orally for 20 weeks as a treatment for atopic dermatitis, itchy and scaly skin rashes. CBD-based topicals may also be beneficial as a treatment for acne.

Attention Deficit Disorder and Attention Deficit Hyperactivity

Attention deficit disorder, ADD, and attention deficit hyperactivity disorder, ADHD are common childhood disorders that can continue through adolescence and adulthood. Symptoms include difficulty in staying focused, paying attention, and controlling behavior, hyperactivity and over-activity.

One main physiological irregularity that causes ADD and ADHD is the brain's shortage of dopamine, a chemical neurotransmitter involved in cognitive processes including memory and attention.

Medications including Adderall and Ritalin, which are molecularly similar to methamphetamine and cocaine, stimulate dopamine, thereby enhancing concentration. The downside of these medications is often undesirable side effects, including jitteriness, anxiety, sleep difficulty, appetite suppression, and a propensity to be quick to anger.

The marijuana researcher, Dr. David Bearman, studied the relationship between the endocannabinoid system and ADHD. He discovered the potential therapeutic value of cannabinoids interacting with the brain's dopamine management systems, without the undesirable side effects of traditional medications. Bearman stated:

Cannabis appears to treat ADD and ADHD by increasing the availability of dopamine. This then has the same effect but is a different mechanism of action than stimulants like Ritalin (methylphenidate) and dexedrine amphetamine, which act by binding to the dopamine and interfering with the metabolic breakdown of dopamine. Put simply, the compounds found in cannabis, called cannabinoids, could potentially correct the dopamine deficiency observed in ADD/ADHD patients if dosed appropriately and administered safely.[89]

Alzheimer's Disease

Alzheimer's disease is a progressive, degenerative disease that causes brain cells to degenerate and die. It destroys memory and other mental functions. It is the most common cause of dementia, a group of brain disorders that results in the loss of intellectual and social skills.

There is no cure for Alzheimer's. Patients and their families generally hope to manage symptoms and seek support services to maintain the patient's independence and functioning as long as possible.

Recent research indicates that cannabinoid-based therapy may not only provide symptomatic relief to patients afflicted with Alzheimer's disease, but may also moderate the progression of the disease.

In 2006, Lisa M. Eubanks, Ph.D., a scientist at the Scripps Research Institute and the Skaggs Institute for Chemical Biology, indicated:

Here, we demonstrate that the active component of marijuana, Δ9-tetrahydrocannabinol (THC), competitively inhibits the enzyme acetylcholinesterase (AChE) as well as prevents AChE-induced amyloid β-peptide (Aβ) aggregation, the key pathological marker of Alzheimer's disease.

THC and its analogues may provide an improved therapeutic for Alzheimer's disease simultaneously treating both the symptoms and progression of Alzheimer's disease.[90]

Maria L. de Ceballos, Ph.D., of the Department of Neural Plasticity at the Cajal Institute in Spain, in a 2005 article, wrote:

> *Our results indicate that cannabinoid receptors are important in the pathology of AD (Alzheimer's disease) and that cannabinoids succeed in preventing the neurodegenerative process occurring in the disease.*[91]

The Mayo Clinic suggests as a treatment for dementia, 2.5 milligrams of the synthetic THC, Dronabinol taken twice daily for six weeks. The indication that synthetic THC is beneficial indicates the likelihood that natural THC from the marijuana plant may also be beneficial.

Amyotrophic lateral sclerosis (ALS) or Lou Gehrig's Disease

Amyotrophic lateral sclerosis, also known as ALS or Lou Gehrig's disease, is a progressive neurodegenerative disease that affects nerve cells in the brain and the spinal cord. It destroys the ability of the brain to initiate and control muscle movement. It results in muscle weakness, wasting, and paralysis of the limbs. As the disease progresses, patients may lose the ability to speak, eat, move and breathe.

The average survival time is three years. However approximately twenty percent of ALS patients live five years, ten percent survive ten years and five percent will live twenty years or more.

Stephen Hawking, perhaps the most famous living person with ALS was diagnosed in 1963 and has survived more than fifty years with ALS.[92]

A 2010 study in the American Journal of Hospice and Palliative Medicine indicated that marijuana shows promise as a viable treatment option to relieve symptoms of ALS. It indicated that regular, controlled doses of marijuana, in the form of oil or a tincture, may actually slow the progression of the disease. The study results included:

> *Preclinical data indicate that cannabis has powerful antioxidative, anti-inflammatory, and neuroprotective effects. This has translated to prolonged neuronal cell survival, delayed onset, and slower progression of the disease.*

Cannabis also has properties applicable to symptom management of ALS, including analgesia, muscle relaxation, bronchodilation, saliva reduction, appetite stimulation, and sleep induction. With respect to the treatment of ALS, from both a disease modifying and symptom management viewpoint, clinical trials with cannabis are the next logical step. Based on the currently available scientific data, it is reasonable to think that cannabis might significantly slow the progression of ALS, potentially extending life expectancy and substantially reducing the overall burden of the disease.[93]

Anorexia

Anorexia nervosa, simply called anorexia, is the acute loss of appetite caused by an irrational fear of gaining weight. It leads to restricted food intake and excessive weight loss. Anorexia can compromise the patient's health. In the extreme it can be fatal, with sufferers dying of heart failure, organ failure, malnutrition or suicide.

Other diseases, including cancer and HIV/AIDS, cause decreased appetite, leading to significant weight loss as well.

The hunger-inducing properties of cannabinoids, particularly THC, are well established. The synthetic THC, Marinol, is often prescribed for the treatment of weight loss associated with HIV/AIDS and chemotherapy. The same result can be obtained from THC derived from marijuana.

Anorexia usually has a psychological component, so treatment with marijuana alone, will not by itself have a sufficient effect. Since many anorexic patients refuse food, marijuana may be beneficial as an appetite stimulant. Marijuana can also be beneficial in enabling anorexia patients to relax, and perhaps be more open with their treatment team.

Marijuana has also been shown to be effective in helping patients with anorexia maintain their weight. In one test, 25 women suffering from anorexia for at least five years were treated with the synthetic Marinol. Weight records collected up to one year after the end of the trial showed that the participants continued to improve their nutritional status without developing addiction or withdrawal symptoms. This study suggests that

Marinol was beneficial for these patients who had longstanding anorexia.[94]

For eating disorders, The Mayo Clinic recommends 7.5 to 30 milligrams of THC, in a tincture form, taken orally for four weeks.

Anxiety

Anxiety is a common condition, and many patients with anxiety disorders experience intense, excessive and persistent worry, often with fear, in response to everyday situations. These feelings of panic are usually difficult to control, interfere with daily activities, and are typically disproportionate to the actual danger. Patients with anxiety disorders can suffer recurring episodes of sudden and intense anxiety, coupled with fear or terror that can peak within minutes. This is referred to as a panic attack.

THC is beneficial for relaxation. A team of researchers from the National Institutes of Health studied the effects of marijuana on patients suffering from anxiety. They found that relief from stress was one of the main reasons why people used marijuana. The study indicated:

> *Marijuana and its derivatives have profound effects on a wide variety of behavioral and neural functions, ranging from feeding and metabolism to pain and cognition...*

> *However, epidemiological studies have indicated that the most common self-reported reason for using cannabis is rooted in its ability to reduce feelings of stress, tension, and anxiety.[95]*

Two studies completed in 2011 tested the cannabinoid CBD in subjects with existing social disorders. In the first study, CBD resulted in a decrease of anxiety. The results of the second study indicated that CBD resulted in a significant change in regional cerebral blood flow.

In 2014, a Vanderbilt University-led team of international researchers, including scientists in Japan and Romania, discovered cannabinoid receptors in the section of the brain that regulates the "flight-or-fight" response. The study conclusion indicated that the existence of these receptors explains why many users of marijuana use it primarily to reduce anxiety.[96]

In noting the potential importance of CB_2 receptors and their relationship to anxiety, a study treating anxiety and depression was conducted by researchers at United Arab Emirates University and, concluded:

> ... *has clearly demonstrated the anxiolytic and anti-depressant effect of β-caryophyllene and its underlying mechanism in a CB_2 receptor-dependent manner in rodents.*

> *The results also support the involvement of the CB_2 receptor in the regulation of emotional behavior and suggest that this receptor could be a relevant therapeutic target for the treatment of anxiety and depressive disorders.*[97]

These studies confirm the promise of both THC and CBD in the treatment of anxiety. A consensus among researchers is that THC targets the CB_1 receptors and can be beneficial at lower dosages, while higher dosages can have a negative effect.

These conclusions confirm the need for further research to determine the optimal combination of THC and CBD and the optimal dosage in treating anxiety.

Arthritis

Arthritis causes inflammation of the joints, resulting in pain and stiffness. Although it can affect people of any age, it is more common among the elderly and tends to worsen with age. There is currently no cure for arthritis, the best hope for many is to slow the disease's progression.

There are several types of arthritis. The most common forms are osteoarthritis and rheumatoid arthritis. Osteoarthritis causes the breakdown of cartilage. Rheumatoid arthritis is an autoimmune disorder that initially targets the joint lining. Infections and diseases including psoriasis and lupus can also cause other types of arthritis.

Conventional arthritis treatments vary with the type and cause of arthritis. The general treatment objectives are to reduce the symptoms and improve the patient's quality of life.

Unfortunately, standard anti-inflammatory drugs are often not effective in relieving the pain associated with arthritis. Many patients turn to steroids and other stronger pharmaceuticals, which are often accompanied by severe side-effects.

The primary benefits that marijuana provides arthritis sufferers are the plant's anti-inflammatory and pain-relieving properties.[98]

In 2004, GW Pharmaceuticals sponsored one of the only clinical trials to investigate the effect of compounds derived from marijuana on arthritis patients. The study was conducted on rheumatoid arthritis patients who reported insufficient relief from traditional medications. After using the company's Sativex, an oral spray containing THC and CBD, over a five-week period, patients reported significant relief from arthritis symptoms, including pain on movement, pain at rest, and quality of sleep.

In 2005, Ethan Russo, MD, Senior Medical Advisor at the Cannabinoid Research Institute, indicated:

> *Science has now demonstrated that the THC component of cannabis is a very effective analgesic and that the cannabidiol component has unique immunomodulatory benefits as an antagonist of tumor necrosis factor-alpha, supporting benefits in treatment of rheumatoid arthritis.*[99]

Research has also shown that patients are able to reduce their usage of potentially harmful non-steroidal anti-inflammatory drugs or NSAIDs, including aspirin and ibuprofen, when using marijuana-based medicine.

Studies also suggest that the endocannabinoid system may play a direct role in regulating bone mass and may protect against the breakdown of cartilage.

A 2006 report indicated that in addition to their analgesic properties, their ability to alter or regulate immune functions, and their anti-inflammatory properties, cannabinoids diminished joint damage in animal models of arthritis. The study identified the presence of two endocannabinoids, anandamide, and 2-Arachidonoylglycerol (2-AG), in the synovial fluid of arthritis patients, but not in samples taken from healthy volunteers.[100]

Endocannabinoids are synthesized and released by the body in response to a variety of biological dysfunctions, suggesting that the endocannabinoid system may be one of the body's natural mechanisms for fighting arthritis.[101]

The conclusion regarding the benefit of marijuana-based medicine for arthritis is that the effect of cannabinoid-based medicines on the CB_1 and CB_2 receptors provides relief from pain and inflammation for arthritis sufferers.

As a treatment for rheumatoid arthritis, the Mayo Clinic recommends up to six sprays of the synthetic THC, Sativex, one daily, before bed. If synthetic THC is beneficial, it's also likely that THC from marijuana will provide similar benefits.

Asthma and Breathing Disorders

Asthma is a chronic lung disease that inflames and narrows the airways. It can make breathing difficult and can trigger wheezing, coughing, and shortness of breath. For some, the symptoms of asthma are a minor nuisance. For others, it can interfere with daily activities. At the extreme, asthma can be life-threatening. There is no cure for asthma, but its symptoms usually can be controlled with conventional medical treatments.

A 2014 study by French researchers found that THC blocks muscle contractions caused by the signaling molecule, acetylcholine. Acetylcholine maintains the airway's muscle tone and also contributes to the contractions that occur in asthma attacks.[102]

In 1973, Donald Tashkin, a lung expert and professor of medicine at UCLA, and his colleagues first discovered the effect of marijuana as a bronchodilator. The results were published in the New England Journal of Medicine. The study found that airways widen in both healthy study subjects and patients suffering from asthma after smoking marijuana. It stated:

> *Marihuana smoke, unlike cigarette smoke, causes bronchodilation (expansion of the air passages) rather than bronchoconstriction (narrowing of the air passages) and, unlike opiates, does not cause central respiratory depression*[103]

Autism

Autism Spectrum Disorder, commonly referred to simply as autism, is a developmental disorder that appears within the first three years of life. The cause of autism is not known, but it is linked to abnormal brain chemistry. Medications have been developed to manage the behavioral consequences associated with autism, but none has been developed to treat the disorder itself.

Research on the benefits of marijuana-based medicine on children with autism has been very limited.

Dr. Paul T. Shattuck, assistant professor at the George Warren Brown School of Social Work at Washington University in St. Louis, and his colleagues, studied the use of psychotropic medication for children with autism. The study results indicated that cannabinoids interacting with the endocannabinoid system, not only proved beneficial in regulating emotion and focus but also served as a neuroprotective preventing the further degradation of brain cells.[104]

While this research was promising and indicated the potential for marijuana-based medicine for autism, there are many who are opposed to the use of marijuana-based medicine by children and young adults.

Bipolar Disorder

Bipolar disorder, also known as manic-depressive illness, is a brain disorder that causes unusual shifts in mood, energy, activity levels, and the ability to carry out day-to-day tasks. Bipolar disorder symptoms can result in damaged relationships, poor job or school performance, and even suicide. Bipolar disorder can be treated,

189

and people with this illness often can lead full and productive lives.[105]

Studies investigating the impact of marijuana use on bipolar clinical characteristics and neurocognition are limited. One study indicated that marijuana may have positive effects for patients with bipolar disorder. Several other studies have reported that for patients suffering from schizophrenia, the use of marijuana improved neurocognitive functioning. The science supporting why a psychoactive drug might provide benefit for patients with a major psychiatric disorder is unclear.[106]

Another study compared the clinical and neurocognitive effects in individuals with bipolar disorder who had a history of marijuana use, compared to non-users. The study demonstrated that bipolar patients with a history of marijuana use had significantly better attention, processing speed, working memory and better neurocognitive performance than the non-marijuana users.[107]

Cancer and the Side Effects of its Treatment Including Nausea

Cancer refers to any one of a large number of diseases characterized by the development of abnormal cells that divide uncontrollably and have the ability to infiltrate and destroy normal body tissue. When left undiagnosed or untreated, cancer frequently spreads throughout the body.

Despite cancer being the second-leading cause of death in the United States, survival rates for many types of cancer are improving due to advancements in cancer screening and new treatment options.

Marijuana-based medicines have proven beneficial as treatment options for the side-effects of chemotherapy, including as an anti-nausea medication and as an appetite stimulant. More promising is early-stage research indicating the potential of CBD in slowing the growth of cancer cells.

Multiple research studies in laboratory animals have shown that cannabinoids inhibit tumor growth. In one study, injections of synthetic THC eradicated malignant brain tumors in one-third of treated rats, and prolonged life in another third for up to six weeks.[53]

Another research study on pituitary cancers suggests that cannabinoids may be the key to regulating human pituitary hormone secretion.

The World Health Organization indicated that tobacco use is the cause of approximately 22 percent of cancer deaths. Since many regular smokers of marijuana are also cigarette smokers. The question was raised whether smoking marijuana is also carcinogenic. Several studies suggest that smoking marijuana is not carcinogenic, although marijuana, when smoked, produces the same tar found in tobacco. One explanation is that while chronic cigarette smokers frequently smoke dozens of cigarettes daily, marijuana smokers generally smoke a very small quantity.

Other studies looked at the link between marijuana use and lung cancer. They concluded that certain compounds in marijuana, including the cannabinoid THC, have anti-cancer benefits.

In 2006, Dr. Donald P. Tashkin published research indicating that heavy tobacco smokers experienced up to a 20-fold increase in the risk of lung cancer, but that frequent users of marijuana were no more likely to develop lung cancer than the average person:

> *The THC in marijuana has well-defined anti-tumoral effects that have been shown to inhibit the growth of a variety of cancers in animal models and tissue culture systems, thus counteracting the potentially tumorigenic effects of the procarcinogens in marijuana smoke.*[108]

In 2012, the Canadian Centre on Substance Abuse, stated in their report, *Clearing the Smoke on Cannabis: Medical Use of Cannabis and Cannabinoids*:

> *There is sound evidence from animal experiments and well-designed clinical trials involving humans that cannabis and cannabinoids are effective for the relief of nausea/vomiting and certain types of pain, as well as for the stimulation of appetite. However, the evidence to date does not indicate that*

they are the best drugs to use for these purposes. Many studies have shown, for example, that for treating nausea and vomiting, cannabinoids are more effective than older medications such as phenothiazines (e.g., Stemetil®) or antihistaminics (e.g., Dramamine®), but appear to be less effective than newer antinauseants such as ondansetron and similar drugs.[109]

A 2013 study in Israel, The Medical Necessity for Medicinal Cannabis: Prospective, Observational Study Evaluating the Treatment in Cancer Patients on Supportive or Palliative Care, stated:

All cancer or anti-cancer treatment-related symptoms, including nausea, vomiting, mood disorders, fatigue, weight loss, anorexia, constipation, sexual function, sleep disorders, itching, and pain had significant improvement... There were no significant side effects to the marijuana except for memory lessening in the 106 patients who continued marijuana use.[110]

In 2013, the National Comprehensive Cancer Network's *Guidelines for Patients Caring for Adolescents and Young Adults*, included:

If medications don't seem to be working, you might want to consider asking your oncologist to prescribe medical marijuana. The active substance in marijuana—a chemical called THC—has been shown to relieve nausea and stimulate appetite in people receiving chemotherapy. Your doctor can also prescribe a medication that contains THC such as Dronabinol or Nabilone. If you choose to go the more traditional route of smoking an occasional joint (or snacking on the occasional pot brownie), be sure to let your treatment team know, and educate yourself about state and federal laws related to the medicinal use of marijuana.

The goal of antiemetic medications is to prevent nausea and vomiting. Hence, antiemetics are typically given before chemotherapy, in which case a pill is an effective form or drug delivery. However, in patients already experiencing severe nausea or vomiting, pills are generally ineffective because of the difficulty in swallowing or keeping a pill down and slow onset of the drug effect. Thus, an inhalation (but preferably not smoking) cannabinoid drug delivery system would be advantageous for treating chemotherapy-induced nausea.[111]

United Kingdom based, GW Pharmaceuticals indicated in an article, Nausea Associated with Cancer Chemotherapy:

A large body of knowledge has now been amassed in this context as a result of state-sponsored studies in the USA in cancer chemotherapy. Pooling available data in some 768 patients, oral THC provided 76-88 percent relief of nausea and vomiting, while smoked cannabis figures supported 70-100 percent relief in the various surveys.[112]

The Mayo Clinic indicates that 2.5 milligrams of THC, with or without one milligram of CBD, for a six-week period, taken orally is beneficial as an appetite stimulant for cancer patients.[113]

The Mayo Clinic also reported:

Studies suggest that marijuana may help reduce nausea and vomiting in people undergoing chemotherapy. However, it may because side effects such as sleepiness and changes in mood. One review suggests that marijuana may cause more side effects in children undergoing chemotherapy than other therapies. However, the effect of cannabis alone is unclear, and further research is needed.[114]

To prevent nausea and vomiting caused by chemotherapy, Nabilone, the synthetic cannabinoid THC, has proven beneficial for therapeutic use as an antiemetic and as an analgesic for neuropathic pain.[1] It has been approved by the FDA for the treatment of chemotherapy-induced nausea and vomiting. While not approved in the U.S. for pain management, it is approved in Mexico for pain.

Northern California-based Jeffrey Hergenrather, MD, who was president of the Society of Cannabis Physicians, an organization representing physicians using marijuana treatment, stated:

Not all tumors are sensitive to cannabinoids. Common lung cancer, and some thyroid and breast carcinomas do not appear to respond well to cannabis treatment. Cancers that have responded include neuroblastomas, certain types of breast cancer, hepatic, renal, pancreatic cancer; colorectal, cervical and prostate cancers, Hodgkins, Non-Hodgkins, and Mantle cell lymphomas, some leukemias, skin cancers, and sarcomas.[115]

The Mayo Clinic recommends various dosages of the synthetic THC, Marinol, to prevent nausea and vomiting caused by chemotherapy, taking it the night before, right before and then after a chemotherapy treatment.

A logical conclusion is that if the synthetic THC pharmaceuticals, Nabilone, and Marinol, are beneficial in treating

---

[1] Nabilone is marketed in the U.S. as Cesamet.

the symptoms of chemotherapy, that natural THC-based medicine from marijuana is also likely beneficial.

Crohn's Disease and Gastrointestinal Disorders

Inflammatory Bowel Disease, IBD, is the chronic or recurring immune response and inflammation of the gastrointestinal tract. The two most common inflammatory bowel diseases are ulcerative colitis and Crohn's disease.

Crohn's disease is a condition of chronic inflammation of a segment of the gastrointestinal tract. It frequently affects the end of the small bowel and the beginning of the large bowel. Symptoms include persistent diarrhea, loose, watery, or frequent bowel movements, cramping abdominal pain, fever, and, at times, rectal bleeding. Most patients with Crohn's disease will require surgery at some point during their lives.

Crohn's patients who used marijuana reported significant relief from the disease's symptoms. They also were able to reduce the amount immunosuppressive medications that had been a mainstay of their conventional treatment.

Dr. Jeffrey Hergenrather, who was named Medical Professional of the year in the Americans for Safe Access' 2015 Excellence Awards, stated:

Patients with Crohn's disease and ulcerative colitis are stabilized, usually with comfort and weight gain, while most are able to avoid the use of steroids and other potent immunomodulator drugs.

Hergenrather also indicated:

Crohn's disease is so debilitating and life-threatening and so difficult to manage with conventional medications it is very encouraging to find that cannabis is proving to be an effective treatment for it right now.[116]

Timna Naftali, MD, a specialist in Gastroenterology at the Meir Hospital and Kupat Holim Clinic in Israel stated:

Cannabinoids influence gastrointestinal motility and, in particular, have an anti-diarrheal effect...[117]

In 2012, the Patient Education Committee of the Crohn's & Colitis Foundation of America (CCFA) stated in its CCFA Medical *Position Statement on Medical Marijuana*:

> *Experimental evidence suggests that endocannabinoids, molecules found in the body that closely resemble compounds found in the cannabis plant, may play a role in limiting intestinal inflammation. IBD patients have been found to have higher levels of cannabinoid receptors in their colonic tissue. Several small studies have shown that a significant proportion of patients with IBD report smoking marijuana to relieve IBD-related symptoms, particularly those patients with a history of abdominal surgery, chronic abdominal pain, and/or a low quality of life index*[118]

In 2012 Dr. Adi Lahat, at the Institute of Gastroenterology and Liver Diseases of the Chaim Sheba Medical Center in Israel in the article, *Impact of Cannabis Treatment on the Quality of Life, Weight, and Clinical Disease Activity in Inflammatory Bowel Disease Patients: A Pilot Prospective Study*, stated:

> *In the present preliminary prospective study, we have found that treatment with inhaled cannabis improves quality of life in patients with long-standing Crohn's disease and ulcerative colitis. Treatment was also shown to cause a statistically significant rise in patients' weight after 3 months of treatment, and improvement in clinical disease activity index in patients with Crohn's disease...*

> *Moreover, the data demonstrated a statistically significant improvement in almost all aspects of patients' daily life. After 3 months' treatment with inhaled cannabis, patients stated an improvement in their health status, their ability to perform daily activities and their ability to maintain social life. Patients reported a statistically significant physical pain reduction during treatment, as well as improvement in mental distress...*[119]

Ulcerative colitis is a chronic gastrointestinal disorder that is limited to the large bowel or the colon. The first symptoms of ulcerative colitis are a progressive loosening of the stool, which generally becomes bloody. Ulcerative colitis is often associated with cramping, abdominal pain, and severe urgency to have a bowel movement. Loss of appetite, fatigue, and weight loss are also common.

In 2011, Simon Lal, MD, Ph.D., a gastroenterologist at Spire Manchester Hospital and Spire Manchester Clinic Hale in the

United Kingdom, in an article, *Cannabis Use Amongst Patients with Inflammatory Bowel Disease* in the European Journal of Gastroenterology and Hepatology, indicated:

> *Patients with ulcerative colitis, in particular, reported using cannabis to improve diarrheal symptoms, and, again, this perceived benefit has received mechanistic support from studies that suggest that cannabinoids inhibit intestinal secretory responses... It is equally plausible to speculate that patients perceived benefit from using cannabis to reduce pain and/or diarrhea because the drug has a direct anti-inflammatory effect on intestinal tissue...*

> *Beneficial effects were reported for appetite, pain, nausea, vomiting, fatigue, activity, and depression. Patients also reported that cannabis use resulted in weight gain, fewer stools per day and fewer flare-ups of less severity...*[120]

Depression

Depression is a mood disorder that results in a persistent feeling of sadness and loss of interest. It affects how sufferers feel, think and behave. Treatment typically includes a combination of medication and psychological counseling. Left untreated, depression may lead to a variety of emotional and physical problems.

Neuroscientists from the University of Buffalo's Research Institute on Addictions found that endocannabinoids may be helpful in treating depression that results from chronic stress.

The study, conducted on rats, showed that chronic stress reduced the production of endocannabinoids. This was linked to reduced feelings of pain and anxiety, increases in appetite and overall feelings of well-being. The reduction of endocannabinoid production affected cognition, emotion and behavior, and may be a reason that chronic stress is a major risk factor in the development of depression.

Dr. Haj-Dahmane, one of the lead researchers found that:

> *...using compounds derived from cannabis-marijuana to restore normal endocannabinoid function could potentially help stabilize moods and ease depression.*"[121]

Endometriosis

Endometriosis is a medical condition that causes the endometrial tissue, the tissue that women shed monthly during menstruation, to spread around the ovaries. Endometriosis can also spread to other parts of the body. The condition results in the formation of endometriomas or endometriotic cysts.

Endometriosis can be characterized by severe pain and irregular bleeding. It may have a significant negative effect on fertility.

Many women with normal menstruation patterns suffer painful periods due to inflammation, however the symptoms of endometriosis are frequently severe. They may include abdominal pain and cramps before and after menstruation, painful bowel movements, pain during or after sexual intercourse and pelvic or lower back pain, vomiting, extreme irritability, and fainting.

Conventional treatment options for endometriosis depend upon the patient's age, the severity of the symptoms and progression of the disease, and whether the patient wants to have children in the future.

One of the main symptoms of endometriosis is pain. It is often treated with analgesics, either over-the-counter drugs such as ibuprofen or if the pain is more significant prescription medications. If the symptoms are minor, hormone therapies are frequently used to prevent endometriosis from worsening, but they are not a cure.

Contraceptive pills can frequently ease some of the symptoms, but they do not prevent scarring nor heal any existing tissue damage. Other treatments include progesterone pills or injections and gonadotropin-releasing hormone agonists, but these may result in serious side effects. If the symptoms are serious and do not respond to other treatments, surgery is an option, with the goal of eliminating tumors or cysts. As a last-resort, hysterectomy is an option.

There is evidence that cannabinoids can ease the majority of endometriosis' symptoms including pain, depression, headache, hypoglycemia, anxiety, fatigue, and inflammation.

Early-stage research indicates that reduced functions of the endocannabinoid system may lead to the spread of endometriosis throughout the body, resulting in increased pain. Preliminary research indicates that endometriosis pain is mediated through the body's CB_1 receptors.[122]

Researchers from Florida State University studied the role of the endocannabinoid system in endometriosis-associated pain. In rodent studies they found that stimulating the CB_1 receptors reduced pain.[123]

Cannabinoids also have properties that can be used to control another main aspect of severe endometriosis, the rapid growth of cells. Early-stage studies indicated that cannabinoids may control cell growth and regulate the migration of cells.[124]

Epilepsy and Seizures

Epilepsy is a disorder that affects the central nervous system, characterized by uncontrollable twitching of the arms or legs and/or seizures. Statistics published by The Epilepsy Foundation indicates that one in 26 Americans will develop epilepsy during their lifetime.[125] For approximately half of patients suffering from epilepsy, the cause of the disorder is unknown.

The objectives of conventional epilepsy treatment are to reduce the disorder's symptoms, through medications and potentially surgery. Even with treatment, an estimated 30 percent of patients who have epilepsy continue to experience seizures.

There are two primary categories of epileptic seizures, generalized and partial. Generalized seizures are produced by electrical impulses throughout the entire brain. These distort consciousness. Partial seizures tend to be produced in a relatively small area of the brain. Seizures can also be a secondary result of a separately diagnosed medical condition.

Patients suffering from all forms of epilepsy usually have chronic and recurrent seizures.[126] Even mild seizures may require treatment since they can be dangerous if they occur during normal activities, such as driving a car. While conventional treatments or sometimes surgery can control seizures for approximately 80 percent of patients with epilepsy, there is no treatment for the remaining 20 percent.

Frequently, children who have epilepsy will outgrow their condition with age.

In 2014, Benjamin J, Whalley Ph.D. of the School of Pharmacy of the University of Reading in the United Kingdom stated:

...most of the available human evidence suggests that both a reduction in incidence and severity of seizures, as well as physical and behavioral improvements in children and adults treated with either cannabis or its 25 preparations (e.g. CBD solution), can be achieved.[127]

In recent years, the successes in using CBD in the treatment of seizures have been significant, but the antiepileptic mechanisms of CBD are not yet fully understood.

The cannabinoid-based treatments for epilepsy include the use of low-THC, high-CBD strains of marijuana including Charlotte's Web, AC DC, Israel-developed Avidekel, and Ringo's Gift.

For seizures, The Mayo Clinic recommends 200 to 300 milligrams of CBD in a tincture form, taken orally for up to four months.

As of the fall of 2015, clinical trials by GW Pharmaceuticals under Food and Drug Administration protocols for the use of CBD as a treatment option for seizures also show progress.

Fibromyalgia

Fibromyalgia is a chronic pain syndrome of unknown orientation. The disease is characterized by widespread musculoskeletal pain, fatigue, and multiple tender points in the neck, spine, shoulders and hips. It is frequently not responsive to standard pain medications.

A study published in *The Journal of Pain* reported that the administration of the synthetic cannabinoid, Nabilone, which mimics the effect of THC, significantly decreased pain in forty subjects with fibromyalgia.[128]

In 2011, investigators at the Institut de Recerca Hospital del Mar in Barcelona, Spain, assessed the associated benefits of marijuana in patients with fibromyalgia. The results indicated that fibromyalgia patients using marijuana benefited from the relief of pain and muscle stiffness, compared to patients who did not use marijuana.[129]

Glaucoma

Glaucoma is a group of eye conditions that results in damage to the optic nerve. It is a leading cause of blindness. The loss of vision is often so gradual that it may not be noticed until the disease is at an advanced stage. The damage to the eye is usually caused by intraocular pressure, abnormally high pressure inside the eye. Symptoms of glaucoma frequently include eye pain, nausea and vomiting, visual disturbance often in low light, blurred vision, "halo" vision and reddening of the eyes.

Glaucoma results in the degeneration of retinal ganglion cells and the optic nerve axons that carry visual impulses from the eye to the brain. Evidence indicates that cannabinoids have a positive effect on a major indicator of glaucoma, the elevation of intraocular pressure, which is regulated by the hydrodynamic systems at the front of the eye.

For glaucoma patients who have not benefited from traditional treatments, marijuana may be an alternative treatment option for reducing the elevation of intraocular pressure and other symptoms.

The use of marijuana use may temporarily relieve intraocular pressure, but it does not cure glaucoma. Marijuana use has been shown to decrease intraocular pressure and has a favorable safety profile. However, it only provides benefits for a few hours before more is needed. The need to use marijuana for the symptoms of glaucoma throughout the day is problematic because the plant's psychoactive effects may decrease the ability to perform normal daily functions, including driving a car.

While not a science-based conclusion, the medical marijuana dispensary, Medicine in Bloom, stated at its website:

> *Medical marijuana's primary benefit for glaucoma patients is its effect on intraocular pressure. In one study, more than 80 percent of patients who smoked marijuana using an ice-cooled water pipe experienced a reduction in IOP of 16-45 percent. Another study used cannabinoids contained in medicinal marijuana, and found a significant drop in IOP in patients who took THC and cannabidiol. A third clinical trial also found that medical marijuana reduces intraocular pressure, as well as blood pressure overall...*

> *The ability of cannabis and THC to lower intra-ocular pressure in glaucoma was serendipitously discovered in the late 1970's by a variety of patients and researchers. Several patients in the US Compassionate Use Investigational New Drug Program maintained their vision while employing large amounts of daily cannabis in situations where standard drug therapy failed...[130]*

In 2004, GW Pharmaceuticals, in an article written by their Cannabinoid Research Institute, stated:

> *The ability of cannabis and THC to lower intra-ocular pressure in glaucoma was serendipitously discovered in the late 1970's by a variety of patients and researchers. Several patients in the US Compassionate Use Investigational New Drug Program maintained their vision while employing large amounts of daily cannabis in situations where standard drug therapy failed.*

> *An emerging concept is that glaucoma represents a progressive vascular retinopathy that requires a neuroprotectant to preserve vision. Some of the resulting optic nerve damage accrues due to NMDA hyperexcitability, an effect that THC and CBD may counter as neuroprotective antioxidants.*

> *Thus, glaucoma is an area where cannabis and cannabinoids may offer particular advantages over available single ingredient ocularanti-hypertensive agents.*

The conclusion is that glaucoma is a medical condition which will likely benefit from the use of cannabis and cannabinoids medicine, and that they may offer particular advantages over available single ingredient ocular anti-hypertensive agents.[131]

The article is no longer available at GW Pharmaceutical's website. It was likely removed because the company intended to proceed with clinical trials under U.S. Food and Drug Administration protocols for cannabinoid treatments for epilepsy, thereby subjecting the company's website, statements, and claims to FDA scrutiny.

The Mayo Clinic has suggested that a single dose of five milligrams of THC as a tincture placed under the tongue may be beneficial in treating glaucoma. The Mayo Clinic also indicates that a dose of 20-40 milligrams of CBD placed under the tongue, as a single daily dose may also be beneficial, however increasing the dosage to 40 milligrams appeared to increase eye pressure.[132]

HIV and AIDS

Acquired immunodeficiency syndrome, or AIDS, is a chronic condition caused by the human immunodeficiency virus, HIV, a retrovirus that invades cells in the human immune system. It weakens the body's ability to fight disease and when left uncontrolled, is life-threatening. While there is no cure for HIV/AIDS, there are medications that can dramatically slow the progression of the disease and have reduced deaths.

Marijuana has become popular as a treatment option for many HIV/AIDS patients trying to manage their pain and other symptoms. Estimates indicate that nearly one-third of HIV/AIDS patients use marijuana for appetite loss, emotional issues caused by the disease, and cachexia, the weakness and wasting of the body.[133]

Most recently, the inhalation of marijuana has been demonstrated in clinical trial data to be associated with increased levels of appetite hormones in the blood of subjects with HIV infection. In animal models, the administration of THC was associated with decreased mortality and ameliorated disease progression, and in preclinical models, cannabinoids have also been shown to decrease HIV replication.[134]

In 2003, Kate Scannell, MD, Co-Director of the Kaiser-Permanente Northern California Ethics Department was quoted in the San Francisco Chronicle as saying:

> *From working with AIDS and cancer patients, I repeatedly saw how marijuana could ameliorate a patient's debilitating fatigue, restore appetite, diminish pain, remedy nausea, cure vomiting and curtail down-to-the-bone weight loss.*[135]

Lupus

Lupus is a chronic autoimmune disease in which the immune system can't tell the difference between healthy tissues and viruses, germs or bacteria. There are many kinds of lupus. The most common type is systemic lupus erythematosus, which affects many internal organs in the body.

As opposed to HIV/AIDS, which results in the immune system being underactive, for patients suffering from lupus, the immune system is overactive, leading it to create antibodies that attack and destroy healthy tissue.

Lupus patients typically suffer symptoms including pain, most notably in their joints. Other symptoms include skin rashes, mouth sores, fatigue, mood changes, swelling of hands and feet, nausea, vomiting, depression, anxiety, seizures, fevers, weight loss, chest pain, hair loss, ulcers, swollen lymph nodes, anemia and abnormal heart rates.

There is no cure for lupus, but its symptoms can be treated with conventional medications, many of which have unpleasant side effects, which are then often managed with additional medications.

While research has been minimal, marijuana has been effective in treating the pain and inflammation symptoms of lupus. It has also proved beneficial in mediating nausea and abdominal cramping that are often severe side effects of commonly prescribed drugs for lupus, including corticosteroids.

Lyme Disease

Lyme disease is the most common tick-borne illness in North America and Europe. It is caused by the bacterium, Borrelia burgdorferi. The ticks pick up the bacteria when they bite deer or mice that are infected with the disease, and then humans are infected if they are bitten by an infected blacklegged tick.

Symptoms in people with the later stages of Lyme disease include body-wide itching and inflammation of the joints. If diagnosed during the early stages, Lyme disease can usually be cured with antibiotics. Without treatment, complications can affect the heart, nervous system, and joints. While some patients can be easily treated, for others it is a never-ending battle.

There is controversy in the medical community regarding what is referred to as post-treatment Lyme disease syndrome, or PTLDS. Some physicians and researchers believe it can be a systemic, debilitating condition which antibiotics cannot be used to treat, and which lacks a general cure. For as many as 10 percent of patients treated for PTLDS, symptoms including severe joint and muscle pain, fatigue, and cognitive difficulties can last for months or even for years. Treatments vary from patient to patient, with no conventional treatment options being available for some patients.[136] Some patients with PTLDS end up in so much pain that they may be bed-stricken for days at a time or confined to a wheelchair.

Later stage Lyme disease can affect the heart and nervous system. Abnormal heart rhythms occur in less than 10 percent of Lyme patients, and heart failure is a rare complication. Facial paralysis, severe headaches, meningitis, confusion, and abnormal sensations in limbs, known as peripheral neuropathy, can develop.

About 60 percent of patients who are not treated with antibiotics in the early weeks of Lyme disease will develop attacks of painful and swollen joints that last for days to months and shift from one or more joints to other joints. Ten to 20 percent of untreated Lyme disease patients will develop permanent arthritis.

Many patients with PTLDS have found that marijuana is one of the most beneficial, long-term treatments to alleviate symptoms. They have found that marijuana can eliminate pain, and provide relief from aches in the joints and elsewhere in the body. Patient experience indicates that the higher the THC level of the marijuana, the more relief that is obtained.

Some sufferers of PTLDS have found that marijuana in a topical form is more effective as an anti-inflammatory than conventional over-the-counter medicines including aspirin. For many, topicals have proven beneficial as a muscle relaxant and to relieve joint pain.

Multiple Sclerosis

Multiple sclerosis (MS) is an immune system disorder in which an abnormal response of the body's immune system affects the central nervous system, including the brain, spinal cord, and optic nerves. The immune system attacks the myelin, the fatty substance that surrounds and insulates the nerve fiber, and the nerve fibers themselves. The damaged myelin forms scar tissue, sclerosis, as referenced in the disease's name. Once the myelin sheath or nerve fiber is damaged or destroyed, nerve impulses traveling to and from the brain and spinal cord are distorted or interrupted.

Eventually, the nerves themselves may deteriorate, a process that is irreversible. Over time, multiple sclerosis patients usually become permanently disabled. As the disease progresses, physical and cognitive disability eventually occur, and in most cases multiple sclerosis is fatal.

The exact cause of multiple sclerosis is unknown. According to the National Multiple Sclerosis Society, the disease is thought to be triggered in genetically susceptible individuals by a combination of one or more environmental factors.

There's no cure for multiple sclerosis, although patients can be in remission for months. Conventional treatments can help speed the recovery from attacks, modify the course of the disease and manage its symptoms. Pain is one of the most debilitating symptoms of MS and remains a challenge to treat with traditional medications.

Symptoms of multiple sclerosis vary widely, depending on the amount of damage and which nerves have been affected. Some patients with multiple sclerosis may lose their ability to walk independently or walk at all. Other symptoms include tremors, lack of coordination, tingling or pain in body parts, partial or complete loss of vision in one or more eyes, double vision or blurred vision, numbness or weakness in one or more limbs, slurred speech, dizziness, fatigue, and sensitivity to heat.

Evidence indicates that marijuana-based medicine can be effective in reducing pain and sleep disturbance in patients with multiple sclerosis related central neuropathic pain, and is generally well tolerated. In recent years, health regulators in Canada, Denmark, Germany, Spain, and the United Kingdom have approved the medical use of marijuana extracts to treat symptoms of the disease.

In 2013, Dr. John Zajicek and his colleagues at the Plymouth University Peninsula Schools of Medicine and Dentistry reported the results of a study which evaluated an oral marijuana extract for treating muscle stiffness in 400 people with all types of MS. In this study muscle stiffness improved by almost twofold in the group taking marijuana extracts compared to the group who were given placebos. Patients given the marijuana-based medicine also demonstrated improvements including a reduction in body pain, spasms and an improvement in the quality of sleep.[137]

A controlled study found that Sativex, GW Pharmaceuticals' tradename for Nabiximols, a marijuana-based tincture in spray form, significantly improved spasticity in some MS patients who had been identified as likely to respond to the treatment.[138] Sativex has been approved in many countries as a treatment for Multiple Sclerosis related spasticity, but not in the United States.

The Mayo Clinic recommends a variety of synthetic and marijuana-based medicines for Multiple Sclerosis. These include combinations of THC and CBD, in addition to hemp oil as a nutritional supplement.

Narcotic Addiction

Narcotic addiction is a chronic disease that causes the compulsive dependence on a narcotic substance. Similar to other chronic diseases, narcotic addiction often involves cycles of relapse and remission. Left untreated, narcotic addiction can result in disability and even death.

When used as prescribed, legal opioids are one of the most effective forms of pain relief, but their use can become dangerous. The Centers for Disease Control has indicated that prescription painkillers, including morphine, OxyContin, and Vicodin, have been tied to almost 60 percent of drug overdose deaths.[139]

Numerous studies point to the critical role of the endocannabinoid system in the neurobiological processes related to stimulant addiction. Cannabinoids can modulate the brain reward systems, and can be beneficial across different classes of stimulants.[140]

One of the reasons that people have such a difficult time ending drug use is due to the severity of the withdrawal symptoms. These symptoms include severe nausea, tremors, and trouble sleeping, all of which may be generally relieved by marijuana. While some consider the use of marijuana to treat drug abuse as simply substituting one psychoactive substance for another, marijuana has been found beneficial in alleviating opioid withdrawal symptoms, resulting in a relapse being less likely.

Parkinson's Disease

Parkinson's disease is a chronic, degenerative disorder that mostly affects the elderly population. Like Alzheimer's, it is thought to be caused by a progressive loss of neurons in the brain. It has also been tied to a dopamine deficiency.

Parkinson's develops gradually, a slight hand tremor is perhaps the most well-known sign. Other early symptoms include a reduced ability to show facial expression, stiffness, slowed movement and slurred speech. These symptoms tend to worsen as the condition progresses. Although Parkinson's disease can't be cured, medications frequently help facilitate walking and other movements and can minimize tremors. These conventional medications increase the body's dopamine level or are a substitute for it.

Recent research indicates that the cannabinoid CBD can help manage symptoms of Parkinson's disease. Conducted by a team of researchers from Brazil, the study reported that daily treatment with CBD led to improved well-being and quality of life among a group of patients suffering from Parkinson's disease.[141]

Post-Traumatic Stress Disorder (PTSD)

Post-Traumatic Stress Disorder (PTSD) is a psychiatric disorder that can occur following the experience or witnessing of a life-threatening event. Examples of such events include military combat, natural disasters, terrorist incidents, serious accidents, or physical or sexual assault as adults or in childhood.

U.S. Vietnam War veterans who suffered from PTSD were found to have problems with family and other interpersonal relationships, with employment, and had increased incidents of violence.

Most survivors of trauma eventually return to a normal life. Some sufferers will have reactions to the stress that do not end on their own, with reactions getting worse over time. PTSD sufferers often relive their trauma through nightmares and flashbacks, have difficulty sleeping, and feel detached or estranged. Many of these symptoms can be severe enough, and last long enough to significantly impair the person's daily life.

PTSD is marked by clear biological changes as well as psychological symptoms. It is often complicated by the development of additional disorders including depression, substance abuse, problems of memory and cognition, and other physical and mental health problems.

Sufferers of PTSD often have problems functioning on a daily basis. They frequently have higher rates of unemployment than the general population. For patients with PTSD, incidents of divorce and separation, spousal abuse and the chance of being terminated from employment are more frequent.

Early diagnosis and treatment are beneficial and may help reduce long-term symptoms. PTSD can be treated with conventional psychotherapy and medication, including antidepressants.

The U.S. Veterans Administration estimates that between 11 and 20 percent of soldiers who served in the Iraq and Afghanistan wars have PTSD, which can cause anxiety, flashbacks, depression and sleep deprivation. About 7.7 million American adults are estimated to have the disorder.[142]

The use of marijuana to treat PTSD gained national attention as thousands of traumatized war veterans have requested access to marijuana from the U.S. government.

In 2014, in the journal *Clinical Drug Investigator*, a team of Israeli scientists detailed the results of their pilot study. Their research consisted of the administration of oral dosages of marijuana to patients with severe PTSD. The study found that marijuana helped alleviate the patients' hyperarousal, a state of increased psychological and physiological tension marked by effects including reduced pain tolerance, anxiety, exaggerated startle responses, insomnia, fatigue, and the accentuation of personality traits. Marijuana also provided the patients with the ability to alleviate their sleep disorders, which is a prevalent issue for many patients suffering from PTSD.[143]

In another Israeli study, published in 2014 in the journal Neuropsychopharmacology, traumatized rats were injected with THC, and did not experience new PTSD-like symptoms after a reminder of the trauma. The researchers concluded that their findings were a significant step in the quest for scientific evidence supporting the use of cannabinoids for PTSD treatment. Dr. Irit Akriav, a psychologist at the University of Haifa, stated:

> *The findings of our study suggest that the connectivity within the brain's fear circuit changes following trauma, and the administration of cannabinoids prevents this change from happening... This study can lead to future trials in humans regarding possible ways to prevent the development of PTSD and anxiety disorders in response to a traumatic event.*[144]

In the United States in 2014, a study was approved to evaluate marijuana as a treatment for military veterans who suffered from PTSD. The objective of the study was to measure the effects of five different potencies of vaporized or smoked marijuana for the treatment of PTSD symptoms. The approval of the study was seen as a major shift in U.S. policy. The results of this study have not yet been released.

Dr. Sue Sisley, an Arizona-based psychiatrist, and a leading PTSD researcher explained that treating the disorder posed a challenge because of the complex array of symptoms:

> *PTSD is such a complex syndrome. It's not just flashbacks and nightmares. It's also depression and anxiety and increased startle response and this whole array of symptoms that are not easily managed with one or two medications. Those who suffer from the disorder are often prescribed 5 or 6 different medications at a time.*

According to Sisley, more than 22 U.S. military veterans are dying daily from suicides due to the effects of PTSD. Based on her experiences with patients, Sisley believes medical marijuana provides a unique opportunity for managing the disorder:

> *The truth is that marijuana can treat the whole spectrum of PTSD symptoms with this one medication," she explains. "The proof is in the clinical response. We're seeing patients who are able to walk away from a lot of their psychiatric medications and their opioids and simply manage their symptoms with one drug — marijuana.*

Schizophrenia

Schizophrenia is a severe brain disorder in which people interpret reality abnormally. It affects a sufferer's cognitive reasoning, behavior, and emotions. Schizophrenia may result in combinations of hallucinations, delusions, and extremely disordered thinking and behavior. It may cause patients to hear voices, see imaginary sights, or believe other people are controlling their thoughts. These sensations can be frightening and often lead to erratic behavior.

Schizophrenia is a chronic condition, usually requiring lifelong treatment. There is no cure, but treatment can usually control the most serious symptoms.

Preliminary research indicates that patients having their first psychotic episode show signs of endocannabinoid deficiency.[145] The results suggest that these patients have lower levels of the cannabinoid receptor CB_2 than healthy patients and have lower levels of the enzymes that make endocannabinoids.

Early-stage research regarding schizophrenia is inconclusive. Some studies suggest that CBD may not benefit schizophrenia patients. Another research study indicates that marijuana users suffering from schizophrenia may have better brain functions than nonusers. However, this studies' results link the long-term use of marijuana to a higher risk of psychiatric problems including bipolar disorder, anxiety, suicidal thoughts, depression, delusions, hallucinations, aggression, and lack of motivation or energy.

In 2012, a research team led by Markus Leweke of Germany's University of Cologne conducted clinical trials which demonstrated that CBD can be as beneficial a treatment option for schizophrenia as antipsychotic medications, with far fewer side effects. The study followed 39 patients with schizophrenia who were hospitalized with psychotic episodes. Nineteen of those patients were treated with the antipsychotic medication amisulpride. The remaining patients were given CBD.[146]

At the end of the four-week trial, both groups showed significant clinical improvement in their schizophrenia symptoms. There was no difference in results from those patients who received amisulpride from those who received CBD. In describing the results, Daniele Piomelli, professor of pharmacology at the University of California-Irvine and a co-author of the study, stated:

Not only was CBD as effective as standard antipsychotics, but it was also essentially free of the typical side effects seen with antipsychotic drugs.

Antipsychotic medications that are currently available often reduce the patient's general motivation and pleasure. They can cause devastating and often permanent movement disorders. The most recent generation of antipsychotic drugs often leads to weight gain and can increase the risk of diabetes.[147]

The study was published in *Translational Psychiatry*. Weight gain and movement problems were seen in patients taking amisulpride, but not CBD.[148]

Dr. John Krystal, Chair of Psychiatry at Yale University's School of Medicine, who did not participate in the research, concluded that CBD had fewer side effects but also seemed to work better on schizophrenia's so-called "negative symptoms," which he indicated were very difficult to treat.

The Mayo Clinic has indicated that 40 to 1,280 milligrams of CBD, taken by mouth daily for up to four weeks, may be beneficial in treating schizophrenia.[149]

Sleep Disorders

Sleep disorders are generally classified as changes in sleeping patterns or habits. Signs and symptoms include excessive daytime sleepiness, irregular breathing or increased movement during sleep, difficulty sleeping, and abnormal sleep behaviors.

Early research suggests that CBD can positively affect sleep. Specifically, it may block rapid eye movement or REM sleep, but this effect may be more related to CBD's anxiolytic or anxiety-inhibiting properties than the direct regulation of sleep.[150]

While the basis for this CBD-and-sleep theory has been identified primarily in rodent studies, there has been some research on sleep-impaired, but otherwise healthy humans.

The Mayo Clinic has indicated that 40-160 milligrams of CBD taken by mouth may be beneficial for sleep disorders.[151]

Glossary

Breeding

The art and science of changing the traits of plants with the objective of producing subsequent generations of plants with certain desired characteristics.

Bud

The flower of the marijuana plant. These are the fluffy parts that are harvested and used for recreational or medicinal purposes as they contain the highest concentrations of active cannabinoids.

Budder

A type of concentrate. The opaque form of hash oil. The difference between wax and budder is subtle, but generally, budder is a softer, pliable product similar to butter at room temperature, while wax usually tends to be crumbly.

Budtender

A worker in a medical marijuana dispensary or retail marijuana store, who recommends, sells and is knowledgeable regarding various marijuana products

Cannabinoids

The chemical compounds unique to marijuana that act upon the human body's cannabinoid receptors, producing various effects including pain relief and other medically beneficial uses. There are 111 known cannabinoids, with more likely to be discovered. The most well-known cannabinoid is tetrahydrocannabinol or THC, which is the most abundant in the marijuana plant. THC produces the psychoactive effects, or the "high" desired for recreational use.

Cannabis

A plant genus that produces three species of flowering plants: Cannabis sativa, Cannabis indica, and Cannabis ruderalis.

Cannabis sativa and Cannabis indica are used to produce both recreational and medical marijuana. Cannabis ruderalis is rarely farmed due to its natural lower THC content and small stature, but there is some cross-breeding thanks to Cannabis ruderalis' unique ability to auto-flower rather than mature based on light, so there is potential for this variety to grow in popularity. Cannabis is native to Asia, but grows almost anywhere and has long been cultivated both for the production of hemp and to be used as a drug.

CBD

The commonly used abbreviation for cannabidiol, one of the at least 85 cannabinoids found in cannabis and second only to THC when it comes to average volume. Recently, CBD has gained support for its use as a medical treatment as research has shown it effectively treats pain, inflammation, and anxiety without the psychoactive effects (the "high" or "stoned" feeling) associated with THC. High CBD strains of Marijuana are being bred more actively and appearing more frequently on the market.

CB1 Receptors

One of the two types of cannabinoid receptors. Both are found throughout the body, but are most common in the brain and immune system. When cannabinoids activate the receptors, they change the way the body functions. CB_1 receptors are responsible for the psychoactive effects of marijuana and affect memory, mood, sleep, appetite and pain sensation.

CB2 Receptors

CB_2 receptors are responsible for the anti-inflammatory effects of marijuana. They are found in immune cells and work to reduce inflammation and immune response, and are a factor in many diseases and medical conditions.

Cloning

A clone is a cutting from a mature marijuana plant which can be replanted and raised to produce buds. Since a clone is the exact genetic image of the mother plant it came from, if the mother plant had any health issues, the clone will have the same issues.

Concentrates

A consolidation of cannabinoids that is made by extracting the cannabinoids from marijuana or industrial hemp. If extracted from high THC plants for recreational purposes, the resulting product has very high THC levels. Concentrates include various products from hashish or hash, thick sticky oils to moldable goo such as budder or wax to resinous bits such as shatter. Referred to by a variety of slang terms, the description of a concentrate is often based on the manufacturing method and the consistency of the final product.

Cubing

Cubing is a way of increasing the frequency in a population for a certain trait. It is not true breeding but it will promote a trait.

Dab

A form of oil extracted from the marijuana plant that is concentrated into an oil that can be ingested. It can also be used as a verb.

Dispensary

A general term used to refer to any location where a patient can legally purchase medical marijuana, the equivalent to retail stores for medical marijuana.

Edibles

Edibles are food products that have been infused with marijuana extracts, usually used for medical benefits. They are commonly baked goods such as cookies and brownies, but options as varied as flavored coffee drinks, breads, and candies exist as well. Retail stores for recreational marijuana and dispensaries for medical marijuana also often sell extract-infused butters or oils for patients or consumers to make their own edibles. Consuming edibles means the active components from the extracts require longer to take effect as they need to be absorbed through the digestive system.

Entheogen

A chemical substance, typically of plant origin, that is ingested to produce a non-ordinary state of consciousness for religious or spiritual purposes.

Flowers

Marijuana flowers are the hairy, sticky, crystal-covered parts that are harvested and dried to be smoked or extracted. While marijuana flowers don't have traditional petals or look like roses, they are still the reproductive organ of female plants. When they are allowed to be fertilized by male plants, flowers will produce marijuana seeds. If they are not fertilized they will continue to produce resin that contains active cannabinoids until they are harvested or begin to die.

Genetic Drift

Random changes in the frequency of alleles, alternative forms of a gene that arise by mutation and are found at the same place on a chromosome, in a gene pool.

Hash, Hashish and Hash Oil

Hash is a shortened version of hashish, which is derived from marijuana plants and can be consumed as a psychoactive or used as a medication. Production involves the removal of the plant's trichomes by a variety of methods including sieving, water extraction or filtering. Once the cannabinoid-laden powder has been collected, it is typically pressed and ready to be used. Hash ranges in potency, but is generally stronger than straight flowers since everything but the active part of the plant has been removed. A similar concentrated product can also be produced chemically using a solvent; however, this product is commonly referred to as hash oil or "honey oil."

Hybrid

A plant that is a genetic cross between one or more separate marijuana strains. Hybrids can happen unintentionally, but they are usually bred specifically to combine desired traits of the original, parent plants. Most marijuana on the market today is some form of hybrid.

Ice

A term used to refer to certain types of marijuana extracts or concentrates.

Indica

The abbreviated name for the Cannabis indica species of cannabis. Compared to their sativa counterparts, the plants are shorter, bushier and have more compact flower structure. This species tends to produce more relaxing physical effects and can have a sedative quality.

Industrial Hemp

Also commonly referred to as hemp. A variety of cannabis sativa that has a long history of use globally. While industrial hemp is the same species as marijuana, it is a separate Cannabis subspecies, and has major differences. Industrial hemp has low levels of THC compared to marijuana strains that have been bred for recreational use as a psychoactive use. Marijuana for recreational purposes can be can consist of 10 percent or more THC, and industrial hemp has a minimal amount, typically less than 1 percent. The reason for the significantly lower percentage of THC in industrial hemp is that most THC is formed in resin glands on the buds and flowers of the female marijuana plant. Industrial hemp is not cultivated to produce buds, and therefore lacks the primary component that forms the marijuana high. Furthermore, industrial hemp has higher concentrations of Cannabidiol (CBD) than marijuana, which research has proven can be beneficial for various medical conditions.

Keef

Either the crystals from high-quality marijuana buds or the yellow pollen from the male plants.

Maconha

Word for cannabis used by slaves and the indigenous population of colonial Brazil.

Marihuana

Alternative and probably the original Spanish spelling of marijuana.

Marijuana

The words cannabis and marijuana are often used interchangeably. Botanically, the plant genus is Cannabis. It has been used for thousands of years by humans, for fiber, oils, medical treatment, religious purposes and recreation. The word marijuana, is generally acknowledged as originating from Mexican Spanish. It is the general term for a cannabis plant which has a high THC content.

Phytocannabinoids

Naturally occurring cannabinoids found in the cannabis plant.

Sativa

The abbreviated name for the Cannabis sativa subspecies of the cannabis plant. In general, these plants originated outside of the Middle East and Asia and include strains that are from areas including South America, the Caribbean, Africa, and Thailand. These strains tend to grow taller as plants (usually over 5 feet), are lighter in color and take longer to flower than indica varieties. When consumed, sativas tend to produce more cerebral effects as opposed to physical and sedative ones.

Shatter

A term used to refer to a specific type of extract or concentrate that typically has a flawless amber glass transparency. It has a reputation for being the purest and the cleanest type of extract.

Sinsemilla

Highly potent cannabis from female plants that are specially tended and kept seedless by preventing pollination. The objective is to force high resin content. The term is also used to describe a very strong form of marijuana which, like skunk, contains high levels of tetrahydrocannabinol (THC).

Skunk

A type of marijuana that contains up to three times as much THC as other strains or varieties.

Strain

A specific variety of a plant species. Marijuana strains are developed to produce distinct desired traits, often high THC for recreational purposes and low THC for medical purposes. Strain names often reflect the plant's appearance or its place of origin.

THC

An abbreviation for tetrahydrocannabinol. It is the most well-known and most abundantly available cannabinoid in marijuana plants. THC is also the component in marijuana that is responsible for the psychoactive effects, or the "high."

Tincture

A liquid marijuana extract usually made with alcohol, glycerol or coconut oil that is often dosed with a dropper. Tinctures can be flavored and are usually placed under the tongue, where they are absorbed quickly. Effects can be felt within minutes. Tinctures can also be mixed into drinks.

Tissue Culture Propagation

A technique used to grow plant cells, tissues or organs under sterile conditions on a nutrient culture medium. It is used to produce clones of a plant in a method known as micro propagation.

Topical

A marijuana-based product where the active properties of the flowers have been extracted and added to a product such as a lotion or a cream that's applied to the skin. The medicinal properties are absorbed through the skin and can be used for various medical conditions.

Trichomes

The resin production glands of the marijuana plant. In Greek the word means "growth of hair," and while these sticky little protrusions can make plants appear a little hairy, they are not hairs, nor are they "crystals," which is how they are often described. THC, CBD and other cannabinoids are all produced in these glands.

Vape

Typically, a verb used to describe using a vaporizer to ingest marijuana.

Vaporizer

A device used to consume marijuana. It heats either flowers or marijuana-infused oils or concentrates to a temperature that produces a cannabinoid-laced vapor to inhale. Vaporizing is healthier than smoking since there is no smoke to ingest, but this method still produces near instant effects.

221

Wax

A form of concentrate. The opaque, crumbly texture seen in hash oil, generally after being stirred over heat to add air.

About Jeffrey Friedland

Jeffrey Friedland is an owner of two retail cannabis stores in Colorado which are located in the mountain resort towns of Breckenridge and Crested Butte, and a cannabis cultivation facility located south of Steamboat Springs. This business was featured in CNN's nine-part reality show *High Profits* during the spring of 2015.

He is also CEO of INTIVA Inc., a multi-faceted life sciences company in the worldwide legal cannabis industry. INTIVA has established operating businesses and made venture investments in the cannabis industry in California, Colorado, Canada and Israel.

Mr. Friedland has been the CEO of a Nasdaq-listed company, a member of the board of directors and chairman of the audit committee of a NYSE listed company, and the chairman of the supervisory board of a company listed on the Regulated Market of the Frankfurt Stock Exchange.

Mr. Friedland was featured or quoted in numerous publications including the Wall Street Journal, USA Today, The South China Morning Post (Hong Kong), NBC.com, Forbes, CNBC and its predecessor, Financial News Network, Bloomberg Information Radio, and Bloomberg TV.

He is also the author of *All Roads Lead to China: An Investor Road Map to the World's Fastest Growing Economy*.

He can be reached at jeffrey@jeffreyfriedland.com.

Acknowledgments

As an owner of two retail marijuana stores and one grow facility in Colorado, and CEO of INTIVA, a multi-faceted life sciences company focused on the global cannabis industry, I quickly realized my need for credible information about marijuana. Much to my chagrin, I found few people who had more than a basic understanding of this misunderstood plant. The idea for this book grew from my "need to know" and to make sure that my knowledge was sound and factual.

I learned a great deal about marijuana during my research and am grateful to my many colleagues, friends and relatives who provided me with encouragement, assistance and suggestions as I wrote *Marijuana: The World's Most Misunderstood Plant.*

Dr. Alan Shackelford repeatedly emphasized the importance of sound scientific and clinical research as the only way to convince skeptics of the great potential for cannabis to be used in treating a variety of disorders and diseases. He was instrumental in my becoming aware that scientific, clinical research is the only way to convince doubters that marijuana has the potential to be a useful treatment for a variety of diseases. Dr. Oded Sagee was key to my understanding that the entire industry is ultimately "about the plant." What I learned from both of them is that there is a desperate need for "real science" in this field.

I owe special thanks to my INTIVA colleagues, Tyler Burpee, Courtney Clark, Josh Greenberg, Michael Kraft, Courtney Price, Richard Greenberg and Evan Wasoff. They as I, are convinced that the global cannabis industry can be considered a new emerging market that has great growth potential.

Special thanks to Alan Talesnick who was always ready and willing to act as a sounding board and was extremely supportive of my involvement in this new industry.

I am grateful to so many others, among them, Cathy Klein, Dr. Jordan Klein, Dr. David Opperman, Leigh Severance, Dr. Ben

Siew and Kevin Wood, who offered guidance and have been enthusiastic supporters and cheerleaders for our business venture.

Thanks also to Miles Begin for the great cover design.

Special thanks to Lorin Cohen for her major role in helping me research, organize, and edit the manuscript. Without her help, I doubt this book would have come to fruition. And finally thanks to my wife, Kathy, who encouraged me in my quest to write this book, and for her support, suggestions final editing and review, and putting up with me during more sleep-deprived nights than I wish to remember.

Index

addiction, 3, 44, 51, 54, 57, 59, 61, 171, 193, 194

AIDS. *See* HIV/AIDS, *See* HIV/AIDS

Amendment 64, v, 80

Anslinger, 3, 52, 53, 54, 56, 57, 59, 62

autoimmune disease, 189

bhang, 35

Bible, 32, 33, 34

Breckenridge Cannabis Club, vii, viii

Budder, 114, 202

cannabichromene, 20

cannabidiolic acid, 20

cannabidivarin, 20, 152

cannabigerol, 20

cannabinoids, 6, 10, 13, 14, 16, 17, 19, 20, 22, 73, 76, 90, 93, 98, 99, 100, 102, 106, 107, 108, 111, 113, 118, 120, 128, 129, 130, 135, 138, 139, 141, 142, 143, 145, 151, 153, 155, 156, 159, 160, 161, 162, 164, 167, 168, 169, 170, 174, 175, 177, 178, 180, 182, 184, 187, 188, 189, 196, 197, 202, 203, 204, 206, 208, 210

cannabinol, 20

CB$_1$, 142, 143, 152, 160, 162, 163, 172, 174, 184, 204

CB$_2$, 142, 143, 152, 163, 172, 174, 198, 204

CBC, 20, 152

CBD, ix, x, 7, 10, 13, 14, 17, 19, 22, 24, 39, 81, 87, 107, 115, 119, 127, 128, 129, 130, 134, 135, 138, 145, 146, 147, 148, 149, 150, 151, 156, 158, 159, 160, 162, 163, 164, 167, 171, 172, 173, 177, 179, 185, 186, 188, 193, 195, 198, 199, 200, 203, 207, 210

CBDA, 20, 151, 153

CBDV, 20, 152

CBG, 20, 130, 152

CBN, 20, 128, 129, 130, 152

Charlotte's Web, ix, 24, 39, 129, 145, 146, 147, 148, 185

Crohn's, 139, 163, 180, 181

Delta-9-tetrahydrocannabinol, 18

Dr. Sanjay Gupta, 79, 129, 133, 142, 146

Dravet, ix, 39, 79, 129, 136, 145, 146, 147, 148

Dronabinol, 69, 169, 178

endocannabinoids, 14, 15, 102, 120, 135, 138, 142, 143, 144, 160, 161, 166, 167, 174, 175, 183, 184, 194, 198

Epidiolex, 134, 135, 150, 158

FDA, 69, 72, 77, 121, 128, 134, 150, 158, 179, 188

Food and Drug Administration, 68, 69, 74, 77, 121, 137, 147, 150, 158, 166, 186, 188

Global Cannabis Ventures, viii, ix, x

GW Pharmaceuticals, 135, 150, 173, 179, 186, 188, 193

hemp, 2, 10, 11, 12, 14, 30, 32, 38, 41, 43, 44, 49, 50, 51, 52, 53, 57, 59, 60, 71, 81, 84, 92, 123, 145, 146, 148, 149, 151, 167, 193, 203, 204, 207

HIV/AIDS, 170, 189, 190

Howlett, 14

Hybrid, 24, 206

indica, 6, 7, 21, 23, 24, 25, 44, 48, 49, 85, 99, 103, 119, 203, 206, 208

INTIVA, x, 211, 212

Israel, ix, x, 31, 32, 33, 105, 134, 137, 138, 139, 140, 142, 149, 156, 178, 181, 186, 211

Kush strains, 25

Lupus, 189, 190

Lyme disease, 190, 191

Marijuana varieties
  Unstable seed varieties, 22

Marijuana Varieties, 21
  Clone-Only Varieties, 21
  Stable Seed Varieties, 21
  wild races, 22

Marinol, 69, 71, 73, 156, 170, 171, 180

Mayo Clinic, 160, 167, 169, 171, 174, 179, 180, 186, 188, 193, 199, 200

Mechoulam, 14, 138, 139, 155, 164

Medical marijuana, v, 147, 187

Multiple sclerosis, 192

New England Journal of Medicine, 74, 175

NIDA, 63, 134

O'Shaughnessy, 39

Parkinson's, 139, 144, 194, 195

Post-Traumatic Stress Disorder. *See* PTSD

PTSD, 136, 139, 195, 196, 197

Roger Adams, 13, 138

ruderalis, 6, 8, 21, 24, 97, 203

sativa, 6, 7, 8, 21, 23, 24, 25, 85, 93, 99, 103, 119, 203, 206, 207, 208

Sativex, 160, 173, 174, 193

Schizophrenia, 197, 198

Shackelford, ix, x, 146, 165

Sisley, 139, 197

Sleep disorders, 199

Terpenes, 20

tetrahydrocananbinolic, 20

tetrahydrocannabivarin, 20

THC, ix, 7, 8, 11, 12, 13, 14, 17, 18, 19, 22, 24, 32, 69, 71, 73, 78, 81, 85, 87, 107, 111, 114, 115, 119, 120, 122, 126, 127, 128, 129, 130, 134, 135, 138, 145, 146, 148, 149, 150, 151, 152, 153, 156, 158, 159, 160, 163, 164, 168, 169, 170, 171, 172, 173, 174, 177, 178, 179, 180, 185, 186, 187, 188, 189, 191, 193, 196, 203, 204, 207, 208, 209, 210

THCA, 20, 153

THCV, 20, 152

Tinctures, 115, 128, 209

topicals, x, 127, 128, 130, 167, 192

Topicals, 127, 130, 131

Trichomes, 16, 17, 209

NOTES

1 Ernest Small, "The Species Problem in Cannabis:Science and Semantics. 2 vols. (Toronto: Corpus 1971).,"

2 J. Sirius, Study: New Cannabinoids Discovered, May 28, 2015, High Times, http://www.hightimes.com/read/study-new-cannabinoids-discovered.

3 Leafly, www.leafly.com.

4 Ernest L. Able, Marihuana: The First Twelve Thousand Years, 1980, (Springer).

5 Alison Mack and Janet Joy, Marijuana as Medicine: Beyond the Controversy, 2001, (National Academy Press).

6 Ethan B. Russo, History of Cannabis and Its Preparations in Saga, Science, and Sobriquet, August 4, 2007, (Chem Biodivers).

7 Alison Mack and Janet Joy, Marijuana as Medicine: Beyond the Controversy, 2001, (National Academy Press).

8 Martin Booth, Cannabis: A History, 2005, (Macmillan).

9 Sara Benetowa (Sula Benet), Tracing One Word Through Different Languages, (Institute of Anthropological Sciences, 1936), Warsaw. Reprinted 1967 In: The Book of Grass. George Andrews and Simon Vinkenoog (eds.), (Grove Press, New York).

10 Book of Exodus 30:22-23.

11 Martin Booth, Cannabis: A History, 2005, (Macmillan)

12 US National Commission on Marihuana and Drug Abuse, "Marihuana, A Signal of Misunderstanding," (1972), http://www.druglibrary.org/schaffer/library/studies/nc/ncmenu.htm

13 National Institute on Drug Abuse (NIDA), "Marijuana Research Findings," (1976), https://www.drugabuse.gov.

14 Martin Booth, Cannabis: A History, 2005, (Macmillan).

15 Lester Grinspoon, MD "History of Cannabis as a Medicine," Statement for hearing by DEA Law Judge, Aug.16, 2005, https://www.maps.org/research-archive/mmj/grinspoon_history_cannabis_medicine.pdf.

16 Joy Shannon, "One of the Most Influential Doctors in Medical Cannabis Research: Dr. William Brooke O'Shaughnessy," March 4, 2015 (Culture Magazine) http://ireadculture.com/one-of-the-most-influential-doctors-in-medical-cannabis-research-dr-william-brooke-oshaughnessy/.

17 Conrad, Chris. Hemp for Health: The Medicinal and Nutritional Uses of Cannabis Sativa, 1997, (Simon & Schuster).

18 Jack Herer, Hemp & The Marijuana Conspiracy, 2010, (Ah Ha Publishing Company).

19 Richard Glen Boire and Kevin Feeney, Medical Marijuana Law, 2007.

20 Harry Hubbell Kane, "A Hashish-House in New York. The curious Adventures of an Individual Who Indulged in a Few Pipefuls of the Narcotic Hemp,"(November 1883, Harper's Magazine, http://harpers.org/archive/1883/11/a-hashish-house-in-new-york-the-curious-adventures-of-an-individual-who-indulged-in-a-few-pipefuls-of-the-narcotic-hemp/

21 Martin Booth, Cannabis: A History, 2005, (MacMillan).

22 US Food and Drug Administration (FDA) "FDA History - Part I," http://www.fda.gov/.

23 Pure Food and Drug Act (1906), National Center for Biotechnology Information, http://www.ncbi.nlm.nih.gov/.

24 Aaron Martinez, "100 Years After El Paso Becomes First City in U.S. to Outlaw Pot, Debate Remains the Same, El Paso Times, (June 2, 2015), http://www.elpasotimes.com/news/ci_28238713/.

25 United Nations Office on Drugs and Crime (UNODC) "The Cannabis Problem: A Note on the Problem and the History of International Action," (January 1, 1962), https://www.unodc.org/.

26 Mitchell Earleywine, PhD, Understanding Marijuana: A New Look at the Scientific Evidence, (2005), (USA: Oxford University Press).

27 "Hall of Conspiracy the Men Who Conspired to Make Hemp Illegal," January 18, 2002, http://www.pages.drexel.edu/~sg85nc8p/pubenem.html.

28 "The Federal Marijuana Ban Is Rooted in Myth and Xenophobia," New York Times, (July 29, 2014)

29 Kevin Murphy and Dan Studney "Reefer Madness History," www.reefer-madness-movie.com

30 William C. Woodward, MD Statement to the US House of Representatives Committee on Ways and Means, (May 4, 1937), http://www.druglibrary.org/schaffer/hemp/taxact/woodward.htm.

31 Mark Eddy, CRS Report for Congress: "Medical Marijuana: Review and Analysis of Federal and State Policies" (Apr. 2, 2010), http://www.drugpolicy.org/docUploads/RL33211.pdf.

32 American Medical Association (AMA), "Report 10 of the Council on Scientific Affairs," (1997), http://www.nocirc.org/position/ama2000.php

33 New York Academy of Medicine, Mayor's Committee on Marihuana, The La Guardia Committee Report, "The Marihuana Problem in the City of New York," (1944), http://www.druglibrary.org/schaffer/library/studies/lag/lagmenu.htm.

34 Molly M. Gill, Correcting Course: Lessons from the 1970 Repeal of Mandatory Minimums, (2008), (Families Against Mandatory Minimums), http://famm.org/Repository/Files/8189_FAMM_BoggsAct_final.pdf.

35 National Academy of Sciences, "An Analysis of Marijuana Policy," (1982), http://www.nap.edu/read/662/chapter/1 (Washington DC, National Academy Press).

36 National Institute on Drug Abuse (NIDA) "Provision of Marijuana and Other Compounds For Scientific Research - Recommendations of The National Institute on Drug Abuse National Advisory Council," (January, 1998), http://archives.drugabuse.gov/about/organization/nacda/MarijuanaStatement.html.

37 US National Commission on Marihuana and Drug Abuse "Marihuana, A Signal of Misunderstanding," (1972), http://www.druglibrary.org/schaffer/library/studies/nc/ncmenu.htm

38 U.S. Supreme Court, Leary v. United States, 395 U.S. 6, (1969), https://supreme.justia.com/cases/federal/us/395/6/.

39 US Drug Enforcement Administration (DEA) "A Tradition of Excellence: The History of the DEA from 1973-2003," http://catalog.hathitrust.org/Record/005952023.

40 US National Commission on Marihuana and Drug Abuse "Marihuana, A Signal of Misunderstanding," (1972), http://www.druglibrary.org/schaffer/library/studies/nc/ncmenu.htm.

41 The Report of the National Commission on Marihuana and Drug Abuse, "Drug Use In America: Problem in Perspective," (1972), http://www.druglibrary.org/schaffer/library/studies/duapip/pipmenu.htm.

42 US National Commission on Marihuana and Drug Abuse "Marihuana, A Signal of Misunderstanding," (1972), http://www.druglibrary.org/schaffer/library/studies/nc/ncmenu.htm.

43 Richard Nixon, LLB "The President's News Conference," The American Presidency Project, (May 1, 1971), http://www.presidency.ucsb.edu/ws/?pid=2995.
44 "Marijuana Warrior Robert Randall: The Life and Times of the First American Who Fought for Medical Marijuana," (April 15, 2015), http://www.weeddepot.com/learn/blog/marijuana-warrior-robert-randall-life-and-times-first-american-who-fought-medical-marijuana/.

45 National Institute on Drug Abuse (NIDA), "Provision of Marijuana and Other Compounds For Scientific Research - Recommendations of the National Institute on Drug Abuse National Advisory Council," (January. 1998), http://archives.drugabuse.gov/about/organization/nacda/MarijuanaStatement.html

46 Frontline, "Busted: America's War on Marijuana," (April 28, 1998), http://www.pbs.org/wgbh/pages/frontline/shows/dope/.

47 Francis L. Young, "Ruling in the matter of Marijuana Rescheduling Petition", (September 6, 1988) http://medicalmarijuana.procon.org/sourcefiles/Young1988.pdf.

48 US Drug Enforcement Administration (DEA) "A Tradition of Excellence: The History of the DEA from 1973-2003," http://catalog.hathitrust.org/Record/005952023.

49 Mark A. R. Kleiman, PhD Richard Doblin, PhD "Marijuana as Antiemetic Medicine: A Survey of Oncologists' Experiences and Attitude," Annals of Internal Medicine, (July 1991).

Richard Glen Boire and Kevin Feeney, Medical Marijuana Law, (2007), (Ronin Publishing),

50 Rosalie Liccardo Pacula, PhD "State Medical Marijuana Laws: Understanding the Laws and Their Limitations," Journal of Public Health Policy, (2002).

51 Proposition P, (November 1991), San Francisco Ballot Initiative, http://www.marijuanalibrary.org/Proposition_P_Nov_1991.html.

52 Michael Isikoff, MA "HHS to Phase Out Marijuana Program," Washington Post, (June 22, 1991)

53 Irvin Rosenfeld My Medicine: How I Convinced the US Government to Provide My Marijuana and Helped Launch a National Movement, (2010), http://www.drumebooks.org/2064008.pdf.

54 Janet Joy, Alison Mack, Marijuana as Medicine: Beyond the Controversy, (Institute of Medicine), (2001), (Washington DC: National Academy Press).

55 Janet E. Joy, Stanley J. Watson, Jr., and

John A. Benson, Jr., Editors, "Marijuana and Medicine: Assessing the Science Base" March 1999 Institute of Medicine, "March 1999), Washington DC: National Academy Press.

56 Mark Eddy, Congressional Research Office Report for Congress "Medical Marijuana: Review and Analysis of Federal and State Policies," (April 2, 2010) (Congressional Research Service), https://www.fas.org/sgp/crs/misc/RL33211.pdf.

57 Jerome P. Kassirer, "Federal Foolishness and Marijuana," New England Journal of Medicine, (January. 30, 1997).

58 Tatiana Shohov, Medical Use of Marijuana: Policy, Regulatory, and Legal Issues, 2003, (Nova Publishers).

59 Janet Joy, Alison Mack, Marijuana as Medicine: Beyond the Controversy, (Institute of Medicine), (2001), (Washington DC: National Academy Press).

60 National Organization for the Reform of Marijuana Laws (NORML), "Active State Medical Marijuana Programs," http://norml.org/legal/medical-marijuana-2.

61 U.S. patent 6,630,507, (Oct. 3, 2007), http://patft.uspto.gov/netacgi/nph-Parser?Sect1=PTO1&Sect2=HITOFF&d=PALL&p=1&u=%2Fnetahtml%2F PTO%2Fsrchnum.htm&r=1&f=G&l=50&s1=6630507.PN.&OS=PN/663050 7&RS=PN/6630507.

62 Associated Press (AP), "AARP Poll Shows Most Support Legalizing Medicinal Marijuana," (December 19, 2004), http://www.mapinc.org/drugnews/v04/n1805/a10.html.

63 The Oyez Project at IIT Chicago-Kent College of Law   "Gonzalez v. Raich," (December 18, 2011).

64 US Food and Drug Administration (FDA), "Inter-Agency Advisory Regarding Claims That Smoked Marijuana Is a Medicine," (April 20, 2006), http://www.fda.gov/NewsEvents/Newsroom/PressAnnouncements/2006/uc m108643.htm.

65 American College of Physicians, "Supporting Research into the Therapeutic Role of Marijuana," (February 15, 2008), https://www.acponline.org/acp_policy/policies/supporting_medmarijuana_20 08.pdf.

66 American Medical Association (AMA), "AMA Policy Manual: Medical Marijuana," (November 10, 2009), http://medicalmarijuana.procon.org/view.source.php?sourceID=134.

67 US Department of Justice (DOJ), "Justice Department Announces Update to Marijuana Enforcement Policy," (August 29, 2013), http://www.justice.gov/opa/pr/justice-department-announces-update-marijuana-enforcement-policy.

68 US Department of Justice, "Policy Statement Regarding Issues in Indian

Country," (October 28, 2014),
http://www.justice.gov/sites/default/files/tribal/pages/attachments/2014/12/11/policystatementregardingmarijuanaissuesinindiancountry2.pdf.

69 "Rick Simpson's Hemp-Oil Medicine," High Times, (April 13, 2013),
http://www.hightimes.com/read/rick-simpsons-hemp-oil-medicine.

70 CheebaChews website: www.cheebachews.com.

71 Maureen Dowd, "Don't Harsh Our Mellow, Dude," The New York Times,
(June 3, 2014), http://www.nytimes.com/2014/06/04/opinion/dowd-dont-harsh-our-mellow-dude.html?_r=0.

72 Lumír O. Hanuš, Roger Pertwee & Allyn C. Howlett, "Early
Phytocannabinoid Chemistry to Endocannabinoids and Beyond Raphael
Mechoulam," Nature Reviews Neuroscience, (October 15, 2014),
http://www.nature.com/nrn/journal/v15/n11/full/nrn3811.html.

73 Maayan Lubell, What a Drag, Israeli Firm Grows "Highless" Marijuana,"
(July 3, 2012), (Reuters), http://www.reuters.com/article/2012/07/03/us-israel-marijuana-idUSBRE8620FU20120703#cg0oBZiPc1FI.syqt.99.

74 Maayan Lubell, What a Drag, Israeli Firm Grows "Highless" Marijuana,"
(July 3, 2012), (Reuters), http://www.reuters.com/article/2012/07/03/us-israel-marijuana-idUSBRE8620FU20120703.

75 Raphael Mechoulam, Shimon Ben-Shabat, Ester Fride, Tzviel Sheskin,
Tsippy Tamiri, Man-Hee Rhee, Zvi Vogel, Tiziana Bisogno, Luciano De
Petrocellis, and Vincenzo Di Marzo, "An Entourage Effect: Inactive
Endogenous Fatty Acid Glycerol Esters Enhance 2-Arachidonoyl-Glycerol
Cannabinoid Activity," European Journal of Pharmacology," (January 21, 1998),
http://www.weizmann.ac.il/neurobiology/labs/vogel/PDFs/98EJP353-23.pdf.

76 Raphael Mechoulam, Shimon Ben-Shabat, Ester Fride, Tzviel Sheskin,
Tsippy Tamiri, Man-Hee Rhee, Zvi Vogel, Tiziana Bisogno, Luciano De
Petrocellis, and Vincenzo Di Marzo, "An Entourage Effect: Inactive
Endogenous Fatty Acid Glycerol Esters Enhance 2-Arachidonoyl-Glycerol
Cannabinoid Activity," European Journal of Pharmacology, (January 21, 1998),
http://www.weizmann.ac.il/neurobiology/labs/vogel/PDFs/98EJP353-23.pdf.

77 Ruth Gallily, Zhannah Yekhtin, and Lumír Ondřej Hanuš, " Overcoming
the Bell-Shaped Dose-Response of Cannabidiol by using Cannabis Extract
Enriched in Cannabidiol," Pharmacology & Pharmacy, (February 2015),
(Scientific Research Publishing).

78 "Study: Plant-Derived Cannabinoid Extract More Efficacious Than Isolated
Compound," NORML, (April 2, 2015),
http://norml.org/news/2015/04/02/study-plant-derived-cannabinoid-extract-more-efficacious-than-isolated-compound.

79 Study: Plant-Derived Cannabinoid Extract More Efficacious Than Isolated Compound," NORML, (April 2, 2015), http://norml.org/news/2015/04/02/study-plant-derived-cannabinoid-extract-more-efficacious-than-isolated-compound.

80 Leland Kim, "UCSF Study Finds Medical Marijuana Could Help Patients Reduce Pain with Opiates," University of California San Francisco, (December 6, 2011), https://www.ucsf.edu/news/2011/12/11077/ucsf-study-finds-medical-marijuana-could-help-patients-reduce-pain-opiates.

81 "Clinical Studies and Case Reports," Cannabis Medicine-International Association of Cannabinoid Medicines, http://www.cannabis-med.org/studies/study.php.

82 Leland Kim, "UCSF Study Finds Medical Marijuana Could Help Patients Reduce Pain with Opiates," University of California San Francisco, (December 6, 2011), https://www.ucsf.edu/news/2011/12/11077/ucsf-study-finds-medical-marijuana-could-help-patients-reduce-pain-opiates.

83 A.T. Evans, E.A. Formukong, and F.J. Evans, "Analgesic and Anti-inflammatory Activity of Constituents of Cannabis Sativa L.," Inflammation, (Volume 4, 1988).

84 Zach Reichard, "Cannabidiol (CBD): Fighting Inflammation & Aggressive Forms of Cancer," (December 20, 2012), Medical Jane Website, http://www.medicaljane.com/2012/12/20/cannabidiol-cbd-medicine-of-the-future/.

85 Cannabidiol, a nonpsychoactive Cannabis constituent, protects against myocardial ischemic reperfusion injury. Am. J. Physiol. Heart Circ. Physiol. Am J Physiol Heart Circ Physiol 2007 Dec 21;293(6):H3602-7. Epub 2007 Sep

86 Conditions," The Mayo Clinic, http://www.mayoclinic.org/diseases-conditions/acne/basics/definition/con-20020580.

87 T. Bíró, B. Tóth, G.Haskó, R. Paus, and P. Pacher, "The Endocannabinoid System of the Skin in Health and Disease: Novel Perspectives and Therapeutic Opportunities," Trends in Pharmacological Sciences, http://www.ncbi.nlm.nih.gov/pubmed/19608284.

88 Oláh A, Tóth BI, Borbíró I, et al, "Cannabidiol Exerts Sebostatic and Antiinflammatory Effects on Human Sebocytes," The Journal of Clinical Investigation. (July 15, 2014), http://www.jci.org/articles/view/64628.

89 David Bearman, "Cannabis Efficacy in Treating ADD & ADHD," Indiana Chapter of the National Organization to Reform Marijuana Laws, (August 5, 2012), http://inorml.com/blog/2012/08/05/cannabis-efficacy-in-treating-add-adhd-david-bearman-md/,

90 Aug. 9, 2006 - Lisa Eubanks, "A Molecular Link Between the Active Component of Marijuana and Alzheimer's Disease Pathology," Molecular Pharmaceutics, (Aug. 9, 2006), http://www.ncbi.nlm.nih.gov/pmc/articles/PMC2562334/.

91 Maria L. de Ceballos, "Prevention of Alzheimer's disease Pathology by Cannabinoids: Neuroprotection Mediated by Blockage of Microglial Activation," Journal of Neuroscience, (February 23, 2005), http://www.jneurosci.org/content/25/8/1904.abstract.

92 Jeremy Laurance, "Mind over matter: How Stephen Hawking Defied Motor Neurone Disease for 50 years," The Independent, (January 9, 2012), http://www.alsa.org/about-als/facts-you.

93 "American Journal of Hospice and Palliative Medicine," (May 3, 2010), http://norml.org/library/item/amyotrophic-lateral-sclerosis-als.

94 A. Andries, J. Frystyk, A. Flyvbjerg, R. Støving, Dronabinol in severe, enduring anorexia nervosa: a randomized controlled trial. September 14, 2013), http://www.ncbi.nlm.nih.gov/pubmed/24105610.

95 "How Marijuana Helps Relieve Stress and Anxiety: The Neuroscience," (December 23, 2013), http://www.leafscience.com/2013/12/23/marijuana-helps-relieve-stress-anxiety-neuroscience/.

96 Bill Snyder, "Discovery Sheds New Light on Marijuana's Anxiety Relief Effects," Vanderbilt University Research, (March 6, 2014), http://news.vanderbilt.edu/2014/03/discovery-sheds-new-light-on-marijuana-anxiety-relief-effects/.

97 Amine Bahia, Shamma Al Mansouria, Elyazia Al Memaria, Mouza Ameria, Syed M. Nurulainb, and Shreesh Ojhab, "β-Caryophyllene, a CB2 Receptor Agonist Produces Multiple Behavioral Changes Relevant to Anxiety and Depression in Mice," http://www.sciencedirect.com/science/article/pii/S0031938414003400.

98 James J. Burston , Devi Rani Sagar, Pin Shao, Mingfeng Bai, Emma King, Louis Brailsford, Jenna M. Turner, Gareth J. Hathway, Andrew J. Bennett, David A. Walsh, David A. Kendall, Aron Lichtman, and Victoria Chapman, "Cannabinoid CB2 Receptors Regulate Central Sensitization and Pain Responses Associated with Osteoarthritis of the Knee Joint," Plose One, http://journals.plos.org/plosone/article?id=10.1371/journal.pone.0080440.

99 Ethan Russo, "Arthritis and Medical Marijuana," (2005), Americans for Safe Access, (Cannabinoid Research Institute) (http://www.disabled-world.com/medical/pharmaceutical/marijuana/marijuanaforarthritis.php.

100 "Cannabinoids as Novel Anti-inflammatory Drugs," US (October 2009), (National Library of Medicine, National Institutes of Health), http://www.ncbi.nlm.nih.gov/pmc/articles/PMC2828614/.

101 E.C. Mbvundula, R. A. Bunning, and K. D. Rainsford, "Arthritis and Cannabinoids: HU-210 and Win-55,212-2 Revent IL-1alpha-induced Matrix Degradation in Bovine Articular Chondrocytes In-Vitro," US National Library of Medicine National Institutes of Health, http://www.ncbi.nlm.nih.gov/pubmed/16536902.

102 "Marijuana and Asthma: What Do Studies Say?," Leaf Science, (February 4, 2014), http://www.leafscience.com/2014/02/04/study-explains-marijuana-isnt-bad-asthma/.

104 Thomas W. Frazier, "Prevalence and Correlates of Psychotropic Medication Use in Adolescents with an Autism Spectrum Disorder with and without Caregiver-Reported Attention-Deficit/Hyperactivity Disorder," Journal of Child and Adolescent Psychopharmacology, (2011), (Center for Autism, the Cleveland Clinic), http://www.ncbi.nlm.nih.gov/pmc/articles/PMC3279713/.

105 National Institute of Mental Health, "What is Bipolar Disorder," http://www.nimh.nih.gov/health/topics/bipolar-disorder/index.shtml.

106 Lindsay Abrams, "Study: Pot May Improve Cognitive Functioning in Bipolar Disorder," The Atlantic, (August 15, 2012), http://www.theatlantic.com/health/archive/2012/08/study-pot-may-improve-cognitive-functioning-in-bipolar-disorder/261140/.

107 Raphael J. Braga, Katherine E. Burdick, Pamela DeRosse and Anil K. Malhotra, "Cognitive and Clinical Outcomes Associated with Cannabis Use in Patients with Bipolar I Disorder," (July 23, 2012), Psychiatry Research, http://www.psy-journal.com/article/S0165-1781(12)00300-9/abstract.

108 Mia Hashibe, Hal Morgenstern, Yan Cui, Donald P. Tashkin, Zuo-Feng Zhang, Wendy Cozen, Thomas M. Mack, and Sander Greenland," Marijuana Use and the Risk of Lung and Upper Aerodigestive Tract Cancers: Results of a Population-Based Case-Control Study," https://admin.publichealth.lacounty.gov/ha/present/Staff_researchpapers/YAn_Cui_Articles/Marijuana_Lungca9.pdf.

109 Harold Kalant, Amy J. Porath-Waller, "Clearing the Smoke on Cannabis: Medical Use of Cannabis and Cannabinoids," (2012), Canadian Centre on Substance Abuse, http://www.worldcat.org/title/clearing-the-smoke-on-cannabis-medical-use-of-cannabis-and-cannabinoids/oclc/812917734.

110 Gil Bar-Sela, Marina Vorobeichik, Saher Drawsheh, Anat Omer, Victoria Goldberg, and Ella Muller, "The Medical Necessity for Medicinal Cannabis: Prospective, Observational Study Evaluating the Treatment in Cancer Patients on Supportive or Palliative Care," (June 2013), Evidence-Based Complementary and Alternative Medicine, http://www.ncbi.nlm.nih.gov/pmc/articles/PMC3730175/.

111 "National Comprehensive Cancer Network (NCCN), (2013), ProCon.org, http://medicalmarijuana.procon.org/view.source.php?sourceID=013111.

112 GW Pharmaceuticals, "Should Marijuana be a Medical Option," (Jan. 2004),
http://medicalmarijuana.procon.org/view.source.php?sourceID=000205.

113 Mayo Clinic, "Drugs and Supplements:Marijuana (Cannabis sativa),"
http://www.mayoclinic.org/drugs-supplements/marijuana/evidence/hrb-20059701.

114 Mayo Clinic, "Drugs and Supplements: Marijuana (Cannabis sativa),"
http://www.mayoclinic.org/drugs-supplements/marijuana/evidence/hrb-20059701.

115 Medical Jane.com, "Physician Profile: Dr. Jeffrey Hergenrather," (March 3, 2015), http://www.medicaljane.com/2015/03/03/physician-profile-dr-jeffrey-hergenrather/.

116 Jeffrey Hergenrather, "Should Marijuana Be a Medical Option?," (July 29, 2009), ProCon.org,
http://medicalmarijuana.procon.org/view.source.php?sourceID=008723.

117 Timna Naftali, Should Marijuana be a Medical Option," (March 12, 2013), ProCon.org,
http://medicalmarijuana.procon.org/view.source.php?sourceID=012259

118 National Association of Drug Court Professionals, "Position Statement on Marijuana,"
http://www.nadcp.org/sites/default/files/nadcp/NADCP%20Board%20Posit ion%20Statement%20-%20Marijuana.pdf.

119 A. Lahat, A. Lang A, and S. Ben-Horin S., Jan. 2012 Digestion article, "Impact of Cannabis Treatment on the Quality of Life, Weight, and Clinical Disease Activity in Inflammatory Bowel Disease Patients: A Pilot Prospective Study," (January 2012), US National Library of Medicine National Institutes of Health, (PubMed.org), http://www.ncbi.nlm.nih.gov/pubmed/22095142.

120 Abbey Ridge, "Cannabis and Irritable Bowel Disease," (May 8, 2015), My Kind of Meds, http://mycm.ca/articles/friday-may-8-2015-1044/cannabis-and-irritable-bowel-disease.

121 Samir Haj-Dahmane and Roh-Yu Shen, "Chronic Stress Impairs α1-Adrenoceptor-Induced Endocannabinoid-Dependent Synaptic Plasticity in the Dorsal Raphe Nucleus," The Journal of Neuroscience, (October 29, 2014), http://www.jneurosci.org/content/34/44/14560.short.
122 Natalia Dmitrieva, Hiroshi Nagabukuro, David Resuehr, Guohua Zhang, Stacy L. McAllister, Kristina A. McGinty, Ken Mackie, and Karen J. Berkleya, "Endocannabinoid Involvement in Endometriosis," (US National Library of Medicine, National Institutes of Health),
http://www.ncbi.nlm.nih.gov/pmc/articles/PMC2972363/.

123 Natalia Dmitrieva, Hiroshi Nagabukuro, David Resuehr, Guohua Zhang, Stacy L. McAllister, Kristina A. McGinty, Ken Mackie, and Karen J. Berkleya, "Endocannabinoid Involvement in Endometriosis," (US National Library of Medicine, National Institutes of Health), http://www.ncbi.nlm.nih.gov/pmc/articles/PMC2972363/.

124 Douglas McHugh, Jeremy Page, Emily Dunn, and Heather Bradshaw, "Δ9-Tetrahydrocannabinol and N-arachidonyl glycine are Full Agonists at GPR18 Receptors and Induce Migration in Human Endometrial HEC-1B," (US National Library of Medicine, National Institutes of Health), http://www.ncbi.nlm.nih.gov/pmc/articles/PMC3423258/.

125 Epilepsy Foundation, "Who Gets Epilepsy," http://www.epilepsy.com/learn/epilepsy-101/who-gets-epilepsy.

126 University of Maryland Medical Center, "Seizure Disorders," (2014), http://umm.edu/health/medical/altmed/condition/seizure-disorders.

127 Benjamin J Whalley, "Cannabis in the Management and Treatment of Seizures and Epilepsy: A Scientific Review, "The American Herbal Pharmacopoeia," (March 12, 2014), http://www.herbalahp.org/documents/press_releases/AHP%20Therapeutic%20CompendiumCannabis%20Epilepsy%20and%20Seizures%20Scientific%20Review.pdf

128 M. Ware, M. Fitzcharles, L Joseph, and Y. Shir, "The Effects of Nabilone on Sleep in Fibromyalgia: Results of a Randomized Controlled Trial," (December 10, 2009), http://www.ncbi.nlm.nih.gov/pubmed/20007734

129 J. Fiz, M. Durán, D.Capellà, J. Carbonell and M. Farre, " "Cannabis Use in Patients with Fibromyalgia: Effect on Symptoms Relief and Health-Related Quality of Life," (April 21, 2011), Plos One, http://www.ncbi.nlm.nih.gov/pubmed/21533029

130 Medicine in Bloom website, http://medicineinbloom.com/

131 GW Pharmaceuticals, (Apr. 4, 2004), ProCon.org, http://medicalmarijuana.procon.org/view.answers.php?questionID=000140#answer-id-000651

132 Mayo Clinic, "Drugs and Supplements: Marijuana (Cannabis sativa)," http://www.mayoclinic.org/drugs-supplements/marijuana/evidence/hrb-20059701.

133 Janet E. Joy, Stanley J. Watson, Jr., and John A. Benson, Jr., "MARIJUANA AND MEDICINE: Assessing the Science Base," (March 1999) Division of Neuroscience and Behavioral Health, Institute of Medicine, (Washington DC: National Academy Press), http://www.nap.edu/read/6376/chapter/1.

134 Riggs, F. Vaida, S, Rossi, L. Sorkin, B. Gouaux, I. Grant, and R. Ellis, "A pilot Study of the Effects of Cannabis on Appetite Hormones in HIV-Infected Adult Men, (November 7, 2011), http://www.ncbi.nlm.nih.gov/pubmed/22133305.

135 Kate Scannell, "MEDICAL MARIJUANA / Mr. Attorney General, Listen to the Doctors and Patients, San Francisco Chronicle, (February 16, 2003), "http://www.sfgate.com/opinion/article/MEDICAL-MARIJUANA-Mr-Attorney-General-Listen-2669856.php.

136 Sumathi Reddy, The Wall Street Journal, "The Mystery of Chronic Lyme Disease," (July 6, 2015), The Wall Street Journal.

137 John Zajicek, Susan Ball, David Wright, Jane Vickery, Andrew Nunn, David Miller, Mayam Gomez Cano, David McManus, Sharukh Mallik, and Jeremy Hobart, "Effect of Dronabinol on Progression in Progressive Multiple Sclerosis (CUPID): a Randomised, Placebo-Controlled Trial," (July 13, 2013), The Lancet, http://www.thelancet.com/journals/laneur/article/PIIS1474-4422%2813%2970159-5/abstract.

138 A. Novotna1, J. Mares, S. Ratcliffe, I. Novakova, M. Vachova, O. Zapletalova, C. Gasperini, C. Pozzilli, L. Cefaro, G. Comi, P. Rossi, Z. Ambler, Z. Stelmasiak, A. Erdmann, X. Montalban, A. Klimek, P. Davies andthe Sativex Spasticity Study Group, "A randomized, double-blind, placebo-controlled, parallel-group, enriched-design study of nabiximols (Sativex®), as add-on therapy, in subjects with refractory spasticity caused by multiple sclerosis," European Journal of Neurology, (March 1, 2011), http://onlinelibrary.wiley.com/doi/10.1111/j.1468-1331.2010.03328.x/abstract.

139 Centers for Disease Control and Prevention, "Prescription Painkiller Overdoses in the US," (November, 2011), http://www.cdc.gov/vitalsigns/PainkillerOverdoses/index.html.

139 S. Olière, A. Joliette-Riopel, S. Potvin, D. Jutras-Aswad, "Modulation of the endocannabinoid system: vulnerability factor and new treatment target for stimulant addiction," (September 23, 2013), Front Psychiatry, http://www.ncbi.nlm.nih.gov/pubmed/24069004.

140 S. Olière, A. Joliette-Riopel, S. Potvin, D. Jutras-Aswad, "Modulation of the Endocannabinoid System: Vulnerability factor and new treatment target for stimulant addiction," (September 23, 2013), Front Psychiatry, http://www.ncbi.nlm.nih.gov/pubmed/24069004.

141 Marcos Hortes, Antonio W. Zuardi, Vitor Tumas, Márcio Alexandre Pena-Pereira, Emmanuelle T Sobreira, Mateus M. Bergamaschi, Antonio Carlos dos Santos, Antonio Lucio Teixeira, Jaime EC Hallak, José Alexandre S Crippa, "Effects of cannabidiol in the treatment of patients with Parkinson's disease: An exploratory double-blind trial," (September 2014), Journal of Psychopharmacology, http://jop.sagepub.com/content/early/2014/09/12/0269881114550355.abstract

142 "Gov't approves study of marijuana smoking to treat PTSD in military veterans," (March 18, 2014), CBS News, http://www.cbsnews.com/news/government-approves-marijuana-study-for-treating-ptsd-in-veterans/

143 P. Roitman, R. Mechoulam, R. Cooper-Kazaz, A. Shalev, "Preliminary, open-label, pilot study of add-on oral Δ9-tetrahydrocannabinol in chronic post-traumatic stress disorder," (August 2014), (US National Library of Medicine, National Institutes of Health), http://www.ncbi.nlm.nih.gov/pubmed/24935052.

144 Nachshon Korem and Irit Akirav, "Cannabinoids Prevent the Effects of a Footshock Followed by Situational Reminders on Emotional Processing," (2014), Neuropsychopharmacology, http://www.nature.com/npp/journal/v39/n12/full/npp2014132a.html.

145 Michele Ross, "How Cannabis Helps Schizophrenia," (January 2, 2015), Impact Network, http://www.theecdf.org/schizophrenia/.

146 F. M. Leweke, D. Piomelli, F. Pahlisch, D. Muhl, C. W. Gerth, C. Hoyer, J. Klosterkötter, M. Hellmich and D. Koethe, "Cannabidiol enhances anandamide signaling and alleviates psychotic symptoms of schizophrenia," (March 20, 2012), Translational Psychiatry, http://www.nature.com/tp/journal/v2/n3/full/tp201215a.html.

147 Maia Szalavitz, "Marijuana Compound Treats Schizophrenia with Few Side Effects: Clinical Trial," (May 30, 2012), Time, http://healthland.time.com/2012/05/30/marijuana-compound-treats-sc,"Schizophrenia-with-few-side-effects-clinical-trial/.

148 F. M. Leweke, D. Piomelli, F. Pahlisch, D. Muhl, C. W. Gerth, C. Hoyer, J. Klosterkötter, M. Hellmich and D. Koethe, "Cannabidiol enhances anandamide signaling and alleviates psychotic symptoms of schizophrenia," (March 20, 2012), Translational Psychiatry, http://www.nature.com/tp/journal/v2/n3/full/tp201215a.html.

149 Mayo Clinic, "Drugs and Supplements: Marijuana (Cannabis sativa)," http://www.mayoclinic.org/drugs-supplements/marijuana/evidence/hrb-20059701.

150 Y. Hsiao, P. Yi, C. Li, F. Chang, "Effect of cannabidiol on sleep combination tests consisting of open field and elevated plus-maze in rats," (August 16,2011), Neuropharmacology, (US National Library of Medicine, National Institutes of Health), http://www.ncbi.nlm.nih.gov/pubmed/21867717.

151 Mayo Clinic, "Drugs and Supplements: Marijuana (Cannabis sativa)," http://www.mayoclinic.org/drugs-supplements/marijuana/evidence/hrb-20059701.

63003182R00158

Made in the USA
Charleston, SC
22 October 2016